D1116946

BOOKS BY ROBIN MCKOWN

*Giant of the Atom—Ernest Rutherford*
*She Lived for Science—Irène Joliot-Curie*
*Marie Curie*
*Pioneers in Mental Health*

# THE FABULOUS ISOTOPES

ARGONNE NATIONAL LABORATORY

*ROBIN McKOWN*

# *The Fabulous* ISOTOPES

*Drawings by Isadore Steinberg*

*HOLIDAY HOUSE. NEW YORK*

(frontispiece)
A glimpse of the Atoms for Peace Program. Young physicist from Turkey, receiving instructions in the operation of an important nuclear research instrument (Reactor CP-5) at one of America's great scientific laboratories.

*SECOND EDITION*

PRINTED IN THE U.S.A.

TO

*MONSIEUR AND MADAME ROGER BUCQUET*

# ACKNOWLEDGMENTS

THE LIST of those who gave advice or provided me with source material for this book is a long one. In particular I wish to express my appreciation to Kenneth J. Mahar, Office of Isotopes Development of the U. S. Atomic Energy Commission; Grace M. Urrows of the Public Information Service of the AEC; Dennis Puleston of Brookhaven National Laboratories; Claude L. Yarbro and John A. Harris of the Oak Ridge Laboratories; R. Hobart Ellis, Jr., Associate Editor, *Nucleonics*; David H. Rest, Director, Food Radiation Preservation Division, Quartermaster Food & Container Institute for the Armed Forces; J. Laurence Kulp, Geochemist, Lamont Geological Observatory; M. E. Jefferson, Radiological Safety Officer of the Department of Agriculture; Monsieur Yves Jaigu, of the French *Commissariat à L'Energie Atomique*; and to Hélène Langevin, daughter of Irène Joliot-Curie and granddaughter of Marie Curie.

My special gratitude goes to Alvin Embry, of the Los Alamos Scientific Laboratory, who had the patience to read the manuscript in its entirety and make invaluable suggestions.

R. McK.

# FOREWORD

TODAY a new type of army is serving humanity—an army of isotopes. It is a mighty army, for it has more soldiers than there are grains of sand on our beaches or leaves on our trees. Yet its soldiers are tiny—so tiny that 1,900 million of them, standing side by side, measure no more than an inch.

Isotopes that are recruited not for war but for the good of mankind are the subject of this book. This peaceful army is a by-product of atomic energy.

Up until a relatively few years ago most people outside of the scientific world had never heard of an isotope or, if they had, could not have told the meaning of the word. The fame of isotopes is spreading now and their importance is widely recognized. Scientists prophesy that the "isotope industry" will in time more than pay the heavy cost of all atomic installations. Its real worth cannot be measured in dollars and cents.

This army of isotopes has regiments working in scientific laboratories, shipyards, factories, in hospitals, and on farms. It wages war on the enemies of mankind: germs, blight, harmful insects. It improves our crops and prevents food from rotting.

It has scouts and it has spies, like any regular army. Because these are so small, they can travel almost anywhere: in the blood streams of living creatures, through the roots and stalks and leaves of plants. Such isotopes signal their location by a special code. They gather information on why some plants wither too soon and on what foods help cows to give better milk.

Neither heat nor cold, fire nor flood daunt isotope soldiers. They shoot "bullets" against their enemies in a steady stream. Like Superman, they send forth rays, powerful enough to go through steel or iron. Sometimes they take pictures. They help manufacturers make better products and on occasion they prevent fires. Sometimes they work with police to help solve crimes. They measure snowfall in the High Sierra and they collect data on the course of ocean currents.

The medical corps of the isotope army is the most valiant of all. It sends advance patrols to find disease in the human body. It launches a massive attack to wipe out certain diseases.

Isotopes must be treated and used with the greatest of care, or they will do damage.

When an atomic bomb explodes, it releases hordes of outlaw isotopes into the air or sea. If there were an atomic war, the outlaw isotopes could destroy most of the life on our beautiful green earth.

What are these isotopes, capable of fearful deeds or of splendid ones?

The answer is surprisingly simple. Isotopes are atoms classified in a certain way. All isotopes are atoms and all atoms are isotopes. That is the first thing to know about them.

Theirs is one of the most interesting stories of twentieth century science. In this book we attempt to tell that story, not only for potential scientists but for all who are curious about what is meant by the expression "peaceful uses of atomic energy."

# CONTENTS

*PART I*

# THE NATURE OF ISOTOPES

UNIVERSITY OF CALIFORNIA, BERKELEY

The action of a particle too small to see can be made visible! This is a photograph of the trail of an electron as it travels circularly in a magnetic field through the gas of a cloud chamber.

# The World of the Infinitely Small

## *Chapter* 1

EXPLORING the nature and structure of the atom is the first step toward understanding isotopes.

Atoms are everywhere. Take a deep breath of air. You are breathing in millions and millions of atoms. Take a bit of toast. You have swallowed millions upon millions of atoms. You eat, drink, and breathe about a billion billion billion atoms a day.

All matter is composed of atoms. The earth, with its plains, mountains, oceans, and the air around it, is made of atoms. So are the moon, the planets, the sun, and the stars billions of light years away.

Atoms are tiny beyond imagination. Three hundred thousand atoms can perch across the width of a human hair. A hundred and ninety million can be crowded in an inch.

To explore the atom is to enter the World of the Infinitely Small. In this strange world, most of the rules which govern our own larger domain do not apply. Gravity, weight, matter, light take on different meanings. No one has ever seen an atom. No one ever will, even under the strongest microscope. An atom is so tiny that light waves cannot bring it into focus of the human eye. It would take about a thousand of the largest atoms in a row to reach from one wave to the next of the shortest light waves we can see.

Each atom is a basic particle of the special ELEMENT to which it belongs. An element is a basic substance of matter. Shiny metals such as gold, silver, and copper are elements. Invisible gases such as hydrogen, oxygen, and nitrogen are also elements.

In nature—that is, in the earth, sea, and air—92 elements are known to exist. You will find a list of them on page 167, with their scientific symbols. Some elements are plentiful, like oxygen, for which the symbol is O, and hydrogen, for which the symbol is H. Others are exceedingly scarce. Of the element astatine, there is thought to be no more than half a cupful scattered over the entire earth's surface.

An atom is the smallest particle into which an element can be divided and still remain the same element. Each element has its own kind of atom.

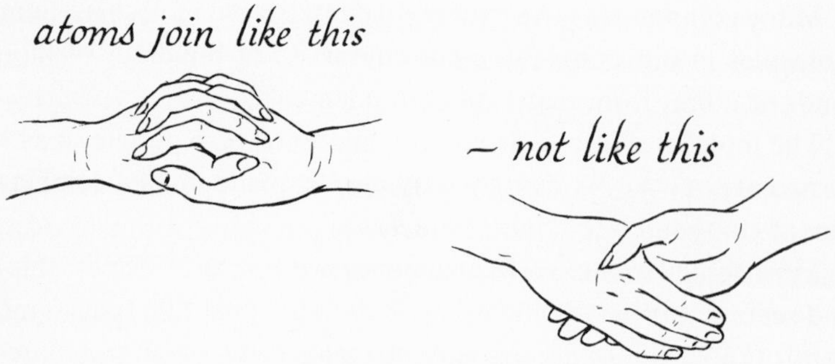

Atoms in a molecule. The electrons of their outer orbits interlace.

Most atoms cling together in groups of twos or threes or more, so tightly it is hard to separate them. These tight clusters of atoms are called MOLECULES.

Some molecules are composed of atoms of the same element. Hydrogen gas molecules consist of two hydrogen atoms. Oxygen gas has molecules of two oxygen atoms.

Most molecules are made up of atoms of two or more elements. Substances composed of such molecules are called COMPOUNDS.

Water is a compound. A water molecule consists of two atoms of hydrogen and one of oxygen. Its formula is $H_2O$. This is so well known that many people when they want to be funny ask for $H_2O$ instead of for a glass of water.

Salt is a compound. Salt molecules have one atom of sodium and one of chlorine.

Carbon dioxide is another simple compound, with molecules made of one carbon atom and two oxygen atoms. Though pure carbon may be graphite or diamond, carbon dioxide is a gas and it forms part of our air. Plants breathe in carbon dioxide; humans and animals exhale it.

Many compounds have extremely complicated molecules. Some molecules in our body tissue are composed of hundreds of thousands of atoms from many different elements.

The molecules of two or more compounds may mingle so as to form a MIXTURE. A mixture may also be made up of a combination of compounds and pure elements.

Most things in the world around us are mixtures. Shoes, ships, and sealing wax, snails and puppy dog tails, sugar and spice—millions of other things are made of mixtures.

An element is made up of atoms all of the same kind.

A molecule is a union of two or more atoms
of the same element or of several different elements.

A compound is made up of molecules.

A mixture is made up of compounds,
or of compounds and elements.

All of these—elements, molecules, compounds, mixtures—are composed of atoms. An atom is a basic particle of which all matter is made.

### *If You Could See Atoms*

If you could see an atom—which you can't—what would it look like? A shiny gold ball for a gold atom? A silver ball for a silver atom? Not at all.

If you could see an atom, it would look as empty as a soap bubble, at least at first glance. There would be nothing there but

s p a c e

Is it possible that an atom is made of nothing? Of course it isn't.

In the center of every atom is a minute speck of matter. This is the NUCLEUS of the atom. NUCLEAR SCIENCE is the study of the atomic nucleus.

Tiny as the atom is, it is enormous compared with its nucleus. If the nucleus were the size of the head of a pin, said Ernest Rutherford, who first proved the atom has a nucleus, the whole atom would be as large as a good-sized lecture hall. Or the nucleus might be compared to a grain of rice in the center of a hundred-foot balloon.

The nucleus is the central core of the atom. Nearly all the weight of matter itself is in this small core. It is therefore incredibly dense. If a marble were packed solid with atomic nuclei ("nuclei" is the plural of "nucleus") it would weigh about 37 million tons. If, by a freak of nature, a huge oak tree were compressed to eliminate the empty space within its atoms, the result would be a mite of dust barely visible to the naked eye, weighing almost the same as the original oak.

If you could see an atom you probably would notice a haze or mist encircling its nucleus. This haze is made up of whirling particles called ELECTRONS. Electrons circle around the atomic nucleus, traveling at such enormous speed they seem to be everywhere at the same time. But each electron is in a definite orbit.

Sometimes the atom is called a miniature solar system, in which the nucleus is the "sun" and electrons are the "planets." Physicists occasionally use the phrase "planetary electrons."

Actually there are vast differences between the laws that govern the large bodies of the solar system and those which prevail in the tiny atom. At normal atmospheric pressure an atom collides with neighboring atoms over 100 million times a second and still holds together, retaining a colossal stability. Should our solar system even pass near a star, like Sirius, all the planets would be hurled from their orbits.

Nor is the atomic nucleus at all like the sun.

Atomic nuclei contain particles, two kinds of which are called PROTONS and NEUTRONS.

Because these, and electrons as well, are included in the atom, and so are smaller than the atom, scientists refer to them as SUBATOMIC particles. There are other subatomic particles, but these three—electrons, protons, and neutrons—are the ones to know for this story.

Atoms of all elements have electrons and protons, and all atoms have neutrons—with the single exception of one kind of hydrogen, as we shall explain later.

Every electron is like every other electron. The same is true of protons and neutrons.

If this is so why are the *elements* so different, one from another? How can gold and silver, lead and mercury, sulphur and oxygen, all be made up of identical subatomic particles?

The answer to that question is one of the many incredible things in the World of the Infinitely Small. Elements are different, one from another, because *each has a different number of protons and electrons in its atoms.*

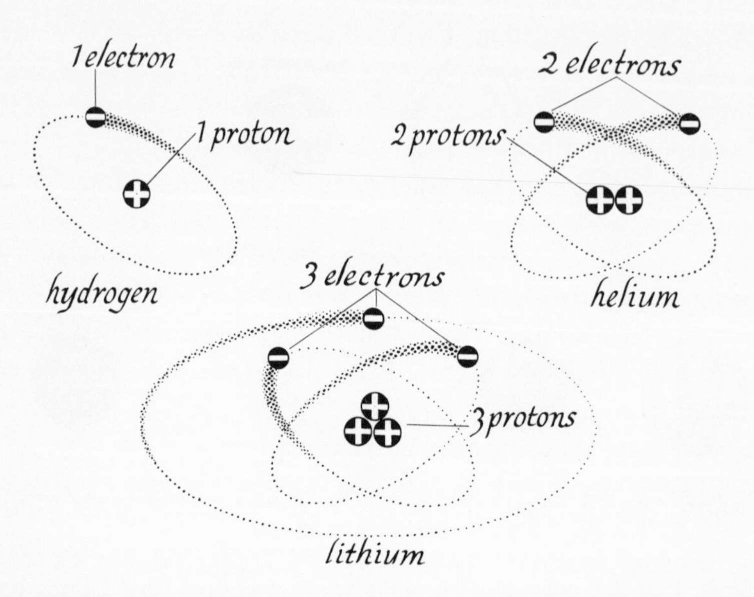


The atoms of three different elements. The number of protons (and electrons) is what makes all the difference.

A hydrogen atom has one proton in its nucleus and one electron whirling around its nucleus.

Helium, another gas, has two protons and two electrons in its atoms.

The atoms of lithium—a soft, very light weight metal—have three of each.

So it goes up to the heavy metal, uranium. The crowded atoms of uranium have 92 protons in their nuclei along with 92 whirling electrons in their orbits.

The number of protons and electrons in atoms decides the type of element. This is the master plan of nature. It is very simple and very marvelous.

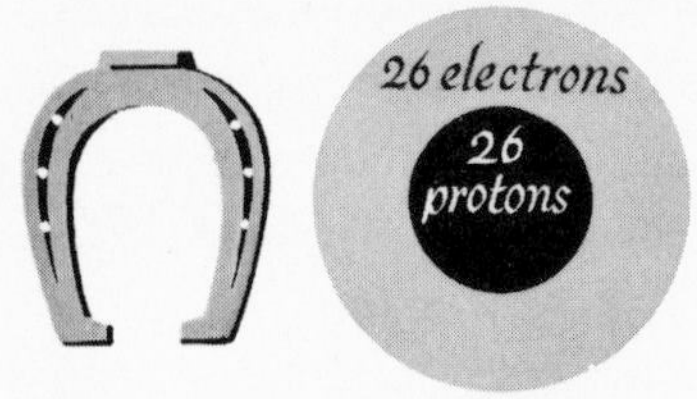


*atomic no. 26, iron atom*

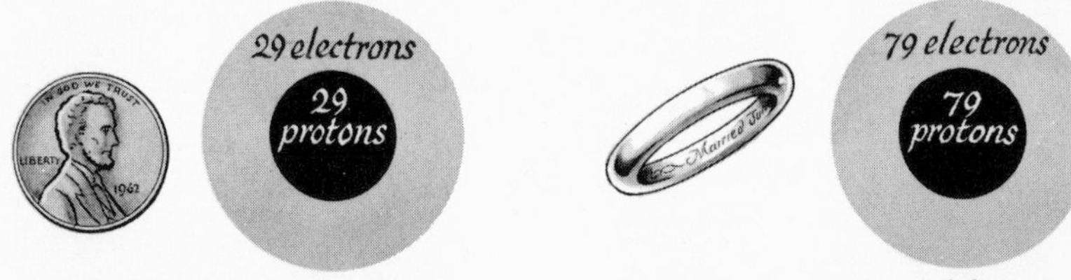


*atomic no. 29, copper atom*  *atomic no. 79, gold atom*

Since it is the number of protons (and electrons) that causes one element to be different from any other, each element is numbered accordingly.

All elements are known by their ATOMIC NUMBER. Hydrogen, with one proton and one electron, is atomic no. 1. Helium is atomic no. 2. Lithium is atomic no. 3. Uranium, with 92 protons and 92 electrons, is atomic no. 92.

You may often see depictions of atoms in diagrams which show the path of electrons as elliptical orbits and the nucleus as a closely packed nest of protons and neutrons.

Such diagrams are not, and are not intended to be, actual pictures of atoms. Regard them only as symbols of atoms, handy to illustrate the number and general location of subatomic particles. Though nature's master plan of the atom is simple, the more you study the atom, the more you will realize its complexity.

You might think that with so many electrons whirling through the atom "sky" there would be frequent subatomic collisions. In a manner that can only be correctly told in the language of mathematics, nature has provided against such accidents.

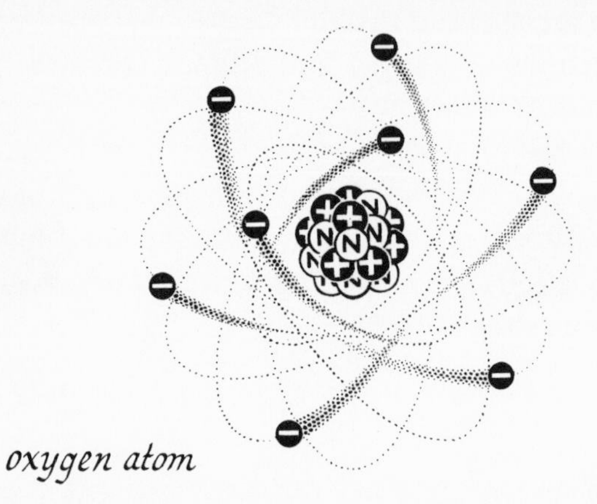


Schematic or symbolic representation of an atom. This one would be oxygen. The speeding electrons would make the orbits look probably like shells of mist, one "shell" within another.

The orbits of electrons are considered as SHELLS—a scientific term—each shell fitting into the next as neatly as in sets of toy wooden Easter eggs.

Each shell can have no more than just so many electrons. The shell nearest the nucleus can have only two. The next can hold eight; the third, 18; and the fourth, 32. We won't go any higher here.

The word "electron" is like the word "electricity" for a good reason. The electron has an electric load, or CHARGE—the technical term. The smallest known unit of electric charge is the electron. The proton also has an electric charge, exactly equal to that of the electron. But the electron's charge is the opposite *kind* to that of the proton. The electron's charge is called "negative," and the proton's is "positive." The symbol for an electron is often the minus sign (−). The symbol for the proton is the plus sign (+).

Substances with the same kind of electric charge repel each other. Substances with the opposite kinds of electric charge attract each other. Thus electrons (negative) and protons (positive) attract each other.

Think of the whirling electron as a girl and of the proton in the nucleus as a boy. An atom with the same number of protons and electrons is as well balanced as a party with the same number of boys and girls. Such an atom is neither positive nor negative, and so as a whole it has no electric charge.

The proton and the electron attract each other because they are opposites. A proton repels a proton, and an electron repels an electron, because in each case they are similars.

### *Neutrons Are Specially Important*

But what about the neutron—the third subatomic particle in the atom? A neutron has neither a positive nor a negative charge. It is entirely neutral, hence its name "neutron." We might say it is neither a boy nor a girl but an "it."

A neutron may change into a proton and an electron. For this reason, some scientists believe that in the beginning of time there were only neutrons in the universe—that a mysterious explosion caused part of these neutrons to break up into electrons and protons, forming atoms of various elements. There is no proof of such a theory. We mention it to show with what respect scientists regard this tiny neutral particle.

The neutron is most significant to this story.

It is because of neutrons
that there are isotopes.

All the atoms of any element have the same number of electrons and protons, but not necessarily the same number of neutrons! The atoms of the same element are exactly alike except in that one thing: their neutrons. Some atoms of an element may have more neutrons than the others, some fewer.

A neutron has a definite weight. The more neutrons an atom has the more it weighs.

This fact enables science to put the atoms of an element into definite classes according to their weights. These classes are what is meant by the term ISOTOPES!

All the atoms having the same weight, thus, are a definite isotope of an element. Those having another weight are another definite isotope of that element.

But what if *all* the atoms of an element have the same weight? They too would be an isotope of that element. Aluminum, beryllium, fluorine, phosphorus, and sodium, for example, are elements that ordinarily have but one isotope each. Nevertheless, each of these elements *can* have more than one isotope. Just how, we shall show later.

Meanwhile, remember that isotopes are atoms regarded in terms of their *weight*. Atoms of the same weight are an isotope of the element to which they belong.

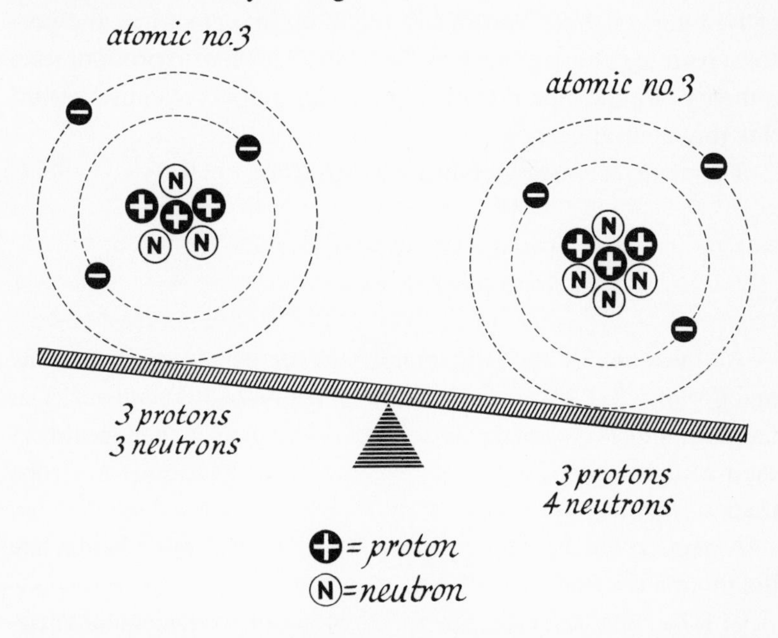


Both of these atoms belong to the same element, lithium. But one atom weighs more than the other. It weighs more because it has more neutrons.

# Atomic Weights and Measures

## *Chapter* 2

HOW DOES one weigh an atom? One cannot put an atom on scales, like a loaf of bread or a slice of cheese. No one can weigh a single atom. Yet scientists, using the laws of physics and chemistry and the rules of mathematics, have worked out not only the actual weights of atoms but of subatomic particles as well. For example, the weight of the electron is .0000000000000000000000000009 grams (27 zeros!). And a gram is only 1/454th of a pound! The electron is so nearly weightless it can hardly be considered as matter at all.

A proton weighs 1,840 times as much as an electron, and a neutron weighs slightly more than a proton. Thus you can see that protons and neutrons make up nearly all the weight of an atom.

In terms of grams and pounds, even the heaviest atom requires a long line of zeros after the decimal point. To avoid such cumbersome fractions, we have the ATOMIC WEIGHT scale. The atomic weight scale is based on the relative weight of atoms.

In 1811, an Italian physicist, Amadeo Avogadro, discovered that oxygen atoms weigh about 16 times as much as hydrogen atoms. On this basis, science gave to oxygen a fixed atomic weight of 16.00, and later, by many ingenious methods, figured out the atomic weights of other elements proportionately.

In 1961, just 150 years after Avogadro's discovery, the International Union of Pure and Applied Physics and the International Union of Pure and Applied Chemistry revised the atomic weight scale. The official standard for atomic weights is now based on Carbon-12, an isotope of carbon. It is assigned an atomic weight of 12 and all other atomic weights are worked out accordingly.

By this new scale, hydrogen, atomic no. 1, is 1.00797. (It is the lightest of the elements, as well as the simplest and smallest.) Uranium, atomic no. 92, the heaviest of the elements in nature, has an atomic weight of 238.03, about 238 times as much as hydrogen. Oxygen now has an atomic weight of 15.9994, instead of 16.00 as formerly.

The disadvantage of the atomic weight scale, in our story of isotopes, is that the atomic weight of an element is the *average* weight of all the atoms in that element. If your teacher announces that your class made an average of 80 in an examination, you don't know whether your grade was 90 or 70, or somewhere in between. In the same way, the atomic weights of the elements don't show the atomic weight of isotopes within each element.

Though it is possible, by modern techniques, to determine atomic weights of isotopes, scientists usually name isotopes, not by atomic weight, but by their MASS NUMBER. Electrons, being so nearly weightless, are ignored, so far as mass numbers are concerned.

Mass numbers are very close to atomic weights. In the World of the Infinitely Small the differences are infinitesimal. In speaking of the atom, people often use the terms "mass" and "weight" interchangeably. Still, there is a real though subtle distinction. *Mass* refers to the quantity of matter. *Weight* refers to the force of gravity acting on matter. A spaceman has a certain weight while he is on earth, but when he is in orbit around the earth, he has no weight at all. Yet in both cases the mass of this man remains the same.

How do we figure the mass *number*? It is really quite simple. Take as an example three isotopes of oxygen. The atomic number of oxygen is 8. All the isotopes of oxygen have the same number of protons; 8 in each atom. The number of neutrons, however, varies. One isotope of oxygen has 8 neutrons, another has 9, and another has 10. If you add in each case the number of the neutrons to the number of protons, you will get the mass number of each isotope:

| | | | |
|---|---|---|---|
| protons | 8 | 8 | 8 |
| neutrons | 8 | 9 | 10 |
| mass number | 16 | 17 | 18 |

And so these three isotopes are named Oxygen-16, Oxygen-17, and Oxygen-18. Or, for short: O-16, O-17, O-18.

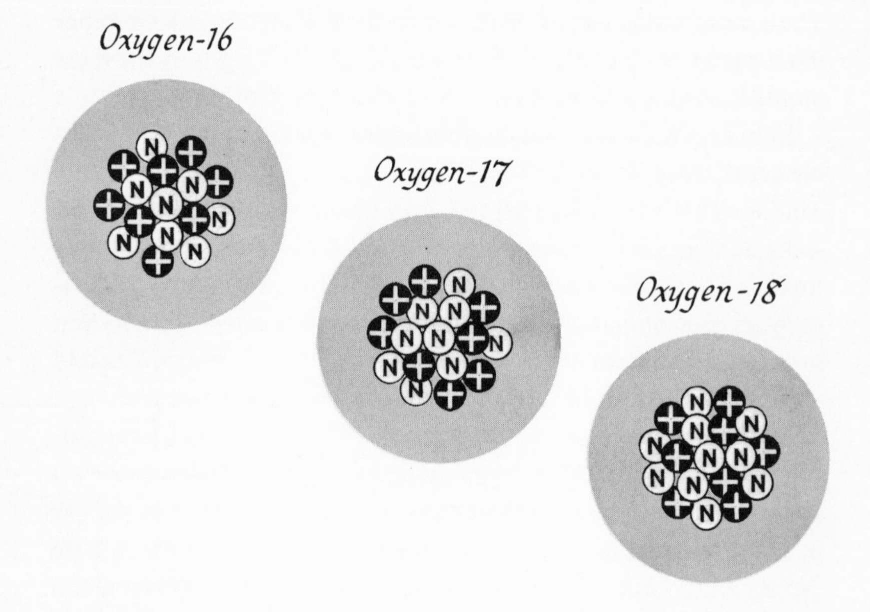


Carbon-12, which has replaced oxygen as the official standard for atomic weights, is an isotope of carbon, atomic no. 6, and has six protons and six neutrons in its nucleus.

Thus far we have considered three ways of naming or measuring atoms: by their atomic number, by their atomic weight, and by their mass number. In a typical symbol of an isotope, two of these designations are used: the atomic number and the mass number. This is the complete symbol for Carbon-12:

$$ {}_{6}C^{12} $$

| | |
|---|---|
| 12 | *mass number* |
| C | *symbol of element* |
| 6 | *atomic number* |

The atomic number is the subscript on the left, and the mass number the superscript on the right. In this book, we shall use only the mass number when we speak of an isotope, thus: Li-7, or Lithium-7.

In nature there are known to be more than 350 isotopes. A few elements, as mentioned on page 25, have only one known natural isotope. That means that all the atoms of these elements have the same number of neutrons. In nature, the element with the most isotopes is tin, atomic no. 50, which has ten. Thus the number of isotopes in the elements varies from one to ten. Elements with even atomic numbers usually have more isotopes than elements with odd atomic numbers, though as yet no one is sure why this is.

With a few special exceptions, which will be mentioned later, isotopes are mixed evenly throughout an element. Some isotopes exist in far larger proportion than others. Neon, atomic no. 10, the gas used for neon lights, is made up of about 90 percent of the isotope Ne-20 and about 10 percent of the isotope Ne-22. Whether you measure a large or small amount of neon, you will find this 90 to 10 percent ratio of the two isotopes.

Of the 350-odd isotopes in nature, only a few are of special interest. Among these are the isotopes of the heaviest element in nature, uranium.

The most plentiful uranium isotope is Uranium-238. Notice that

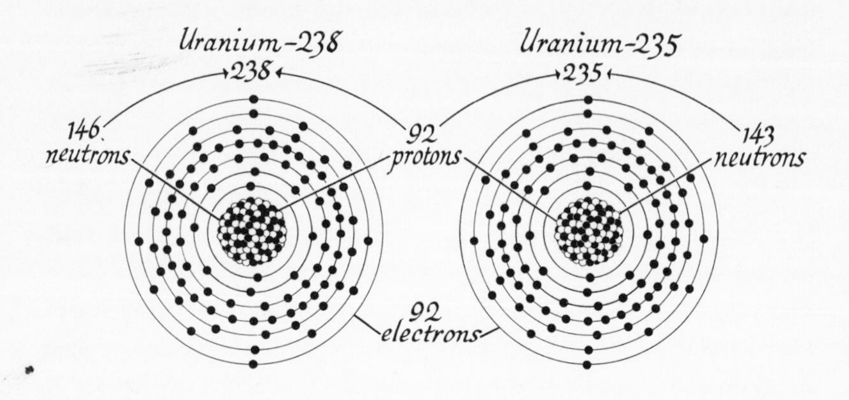


Comparing two important isotopes of uranium.

the mass number here is very close to uranium's atomic weight, which is 238.03. U-238 has an enormous nucleus, the largest found in nature, with 92 protons and 146 neutrons:

| | |
|---|---|
| | 92 protons |
| | 146 neutrons |
| mass number | 238 |

One out of some 140 uranium atoms has only 143 neutrons. This is Uranium-235:

| | |
|---|---|
| | 92 protons |
| | 143 neutrons |
| mass number | 235 |

No isotope has more claim to fame than U-235. It made possible the atomic bomb which fell over Hiroshima. It also has peacetime uses.

Hydrogen has three isotopes. Most hydrogen atoms have one proton and no neutron in their nuclei. This principal isotope of hydrogen is Hydrogen-1, sometimes called protium. Hydrogen-1 is the only isotope without neutrons.

One hydrogen atom in about 6,000 has a nucleus of one proton and one neutron. If hydrogen atoms were eggs, 5,999 would have a single yolk. One would have a double yolk.

The mass number of this "double-yolked" isotope is the symbol H-2. It also has a special name, DEUTERIUM (from the Greek word *deuteros,* which means secondary). Deuterium is almost twice as heavy as protium, H-1, and is usually called HEAVY HYDROGEN. Water which has gone through a separation process so that its molecules contain deuterium instead of ordinary hydrogen is called HEAVY WATER. The discovery of heavy hydrogen indirectly led to the making of the hydrogen bomb. Heavy hydrogen has peacetime uses, too.

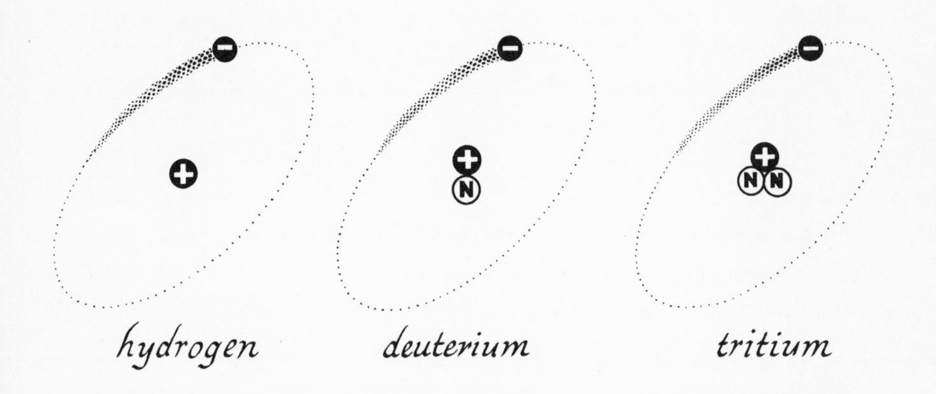


The three isotopes of hydrogen. H-1, ordinary hydrogen, has no neutrons. H-2, deuterium, has one. H-3, tritium, has two. The H-1 atom is the lightest and simplest of all atoms. For this reason, hydrogen was considered as first in the order of elements, and its nucleus was regarded as the primary particle of matter. Hence, the name *proton,* from the Greek word for "first."

The third isotope of hydrogen has two neutrons in its atomic nuclei, plus one proton. This is Hydrogen-3, better known as TRITIUM. It is also spoken of as "triple-weight hydrogen." In nature tritium is even rarer than an egg with three yolks. There is only about one tritium atom in a billion or more other hydrogen atoms.

There is one more way in which atoms are designated. This is by their place in the PERIODIC TABLE. (See pages 170-171.)

## *The Marvelous Periodic Table*

Every element has a place in the Periodic Table, as well marked as the place cards for the guests at a formal banquet. Actually the Periodic Table is a chart, on which the elements are listed horizontally in the order of their atomic numbers and vertically by their *similarities.*

Although all elements are different, some have similar characteristics. Lithium, sodium, and potassium are all soft and shiny metals in their pure form. They are invariably found mixed with other elements in compounds. Because they unite so easily with other elements, they are called "active" metals. We might say they are sociable. They like to mix with their neighbor elements.

The atomic numbers of lithium, sodium, and potassium are respectively 3, 11, and 19. They are eight numbers apart, like octaves on a piano. In the Periodic Table, they are in a vertical column, one under another.

Or take three other elements: helium, neon, and argon. These are called "noble" gases. The noble gases do not combine with other elements and form a compound. They are found in pure form. Like the nobility, they keep to themselves. They are known also as "inert" gases, because their atoms will not budge to unite with the atoms of other elements. These inert atoms are so offish, in fact, they won't even unite with their comrades in the same element! So each atom itself is virtually a whole molecule of one of these noble gases.

The atomic numbers of helium, neon, and argon are 2, 10, and 18. Note that they are eight numbers apart. They too appear one under another in a vertical column of the Periodic Table. There are many such similarities among the elements. Surprisingly, they occur at regular intervals—of 8 or 18 or 32.

The fact that all the elements could be arranged according to their similarities was first discovered in 1869 by a Russian scientist named Dimitri Mendeleev. Since atomic numbers were then unknown, his horizontal columns listed the elements in the order of their atomic weights. Since only some 60 had been discovered in his time, his Periodic Table was incomplete. But he was so confident he had hit upon one of the great mysteries of nature that he left blank spaces for three undiscovered elements, and even prophesied what these missing elements would be like! Later all three were found, with the same chemical properties he had indicated.

| NOBLE (INERT) GASES |
|---|
| 2 He |
| 10 Ne |
| 18 Ar |
| 36 Kr |
| 54 Xe |
| 86 Rn |

Mendeleev's Periodic Table was given modern dress by a brilliant young Englishman, Henry Moseley, around the year of 1913. Through intricate experiments, Moseley discovered that there is a "fundamental quality" in the atom "which increases by regular steps as we pass from one element to the next." This "fundamental quality" is a positive and a negative electric charge: one proton and one electron. Moseley was the one who discovered nature's master plan mentioned on page 20, the Law of Atomic Numbers. In his revised Periodic Table there was room for 92 elements. The seven not yet discovered turned up afterwards.

Shortly after Moseley completed this great work, the First World War broke out. He enlisted as a signaling officer and was killed in the battle of Gallipoli, a tragic loss to science.

A simple version of Moseley's revised Periodic Table is shown on pages 170-171. Chemists sometimes call this the key to the universe. In innumerable ways it aids them in their study of the nature of matter.

ON THE BASIS of what we have covered in this section, it is now possible to give a complete definition of isotopes:

> Isotopes are atoms which have the same place in the Periodic Table as other atoms of their element but which have a different atomic weight.

How did isotopes get their strange name?

The existence of isotopes was discovered between 1911 and 1913 by three scientists, working independently in different countries: Frederick Soddy in England, Theodore W. Richards in America, and Kasimir Fajans, a Polish scientist working in Germany.

Of these three, it was Frederick Soddy who gave isotopes their name. A woman schoolteacher who knew Greek suggested it to him. He had told her that certain atoms had the same place on the Periodic Table but had a different atomic weight. She suggested he call such atoms "isotopes," after two Greek words, *isos* and *topos,* meaning "same place."

With some exceptions, isotopes are mixed fairly evenly within their element. After isotopes were discovered, scientists set to work on finding ways to separate them and to measure their relative proportions within their elements. In 1919 an English scientist, Francis William Aston, invented an instrument which he called the mass spectrograph. By it he succeeded in separating two isotopes of the gas neon, of mass 20 and mass 22. Later he successfully isolated isotopes of other nonmetallic elements by the same apparatus.

In America, about the same time, A. J. Dempster designed an instrument based on a somewhat different principle, called the mass spectrometer, to measure isotopes in metallic elements, such as lithium, magnesium, potassium, calcium, and zinc. The mass spectrograph and the mass spectrometer were predecessors to much more powerful and complicated "isotope separators," which would be put to use in later years.

With the discovery of how to separate isotopes came the first inkling that one day practical uses might be found for them.

# The Miracle of Radioactivity

## *Chapter* 3

THE ELECTRONS in the atom are restless. They whirl around the nucleus so fast they seem to be everywhere at once and no place at a particular time. The single electron of the hydrogen atom makes a billion trips around its orbit in a millionth of a second!

Sometimes, when electrons are hot or excited (literally), they leap (figuratively) from one shell to another.

When atoms unite to make molecules, one or more electrons from the outer shell of one of the atoms jumps over to the outer shell of an adjoining atom. Thus, atoms in molecules borrow or lend electrons.

Shuffle across a thick carpet and you shear electrons away from atoms within the carpet. *You* become electrically charged. That is why you get an electric shock when you touch a doorknob or some other metal object. Stroke the fur of your cat in the dark and you may see sparks shoot out, caused by escaping electrons. There are any number of ways to tempt electrons away from their atoms. Electricity is made up of electrons that have left their atom home as merrily as the children of Hamelin followed the Pied Piper. When there are as many electrons as protons in an "atom home," there is a balance, as we said on page 23. But what happens to that "home" when an electron "runs away"—or when one is "adopted"?

An atom which loses an electron becomes positively charged. An atom which gains an electron becomes negatively charged. Such atoms are called IONS. An ion is really an incomplete atom, with one too many or too few electrons. In either case, it is an atom with an electric charge.

In contrast with the restless electrons, the protons and neutrons are stay-at-homes. Even so, they don't keep still. Within the limits of the atomic nucleus, they too move; they have their own system of rotation. In a *stable* atom, they do not venture beyond that nucleus.

Heat, cold, electricity do not bother stable atoms one whit. They can be blown up in explosions or shot up in volcanos or subjected to the most drastic chemical treatments, yet their neutrons and protons still cling staunchly together in their atomic nuclei. Cosmic rays, which come from somewhere in outer space, are almost the only natural force that can disturb them.

For the most part, the stable atom has the same number of protons and neutrons it had several billions of years ago when the world was new. It does not age. It does not die. In this long period, oceans have formed and have dried up. The earth's crust has cracked and great mountains have risen. The first forms of life appeared in a fashion no one yet understands. Dinosaurs and other monstrous creatures have wandered the earth and vanished. In the last few thousand years—a small fraction of the earth's history—man has become civilized, built towns, churches, factories, schools, and skyscrapers.

None of these vast changes has affected the *stable* atom. In combination with other atoms it assumes a million forms and yet it is still the same. It has the same number of protons and neutrons as it always had.

### *Stable and Unstable*

Notice that we keep saying "*stable*" atom. Not all atoms are stable. The tight little nucleus of certain atoms seems to explode at times. Such atoms are said to "decay" or "disintegrate." This phenomenon of breaking down, decaying, or disintegrating in atoms is called RADIOACTIVITY.

Radioactive elements are those in which a certain portion of the atomic nuclei are continually disintegrating. All the heavier elements—beginning with polonium, atomic no. 84—are radioactive. All the isotopes of these heavier elements are radioactive. The lighter elements—up through bismuth, atomic no. 83—are mostly stable, or non-radioactive. But *some* lighter elements have NATURAL RADIOACTIVE ISOTOPES. Carbon-14, atomic no. six, and Potassium-40, atomic no. 19, are natural radioactive isotopes which in nature are mixed with the other stable isotopes of their element. So is tritium, the third isotope of hydrogen, which exists in a proportion of about one to a billion other hydrogen atoms.

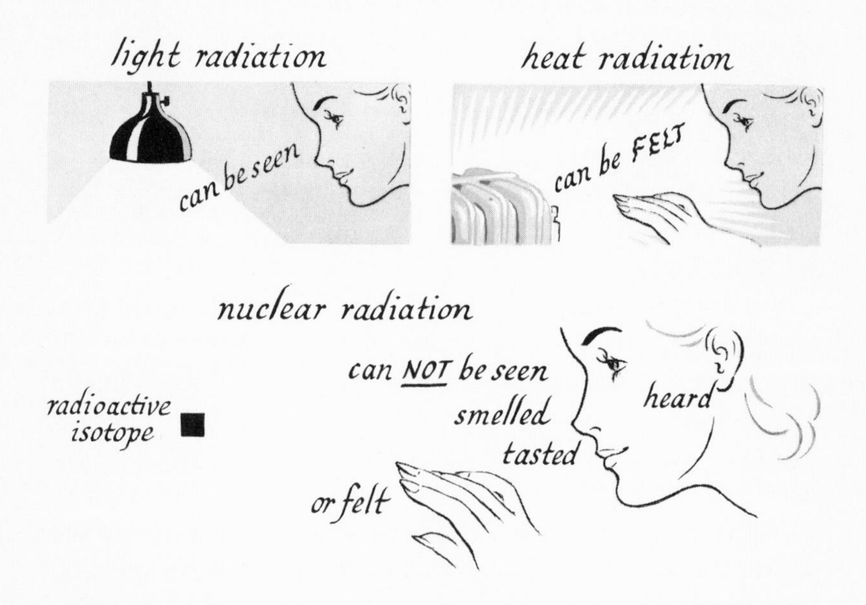


We cannot see, hear, or feel the atoms which disintegrate in a radioactive substance. Only because they send out RADIATION do we know that they disintegrate. Radiation from radioactivity can be detected by a Geiger counter or other instrument. People carry a Geiger counter when they prospect for uranium. It clicks when it comes near this radioactive element.

The radiation of radioactivity comes from three types of rays. They are called ALPHA, BETA, and GAMMA RAYS, after the first three letters of the Greek alphabet: $\alpha$, $\beta$, $\gamma$.

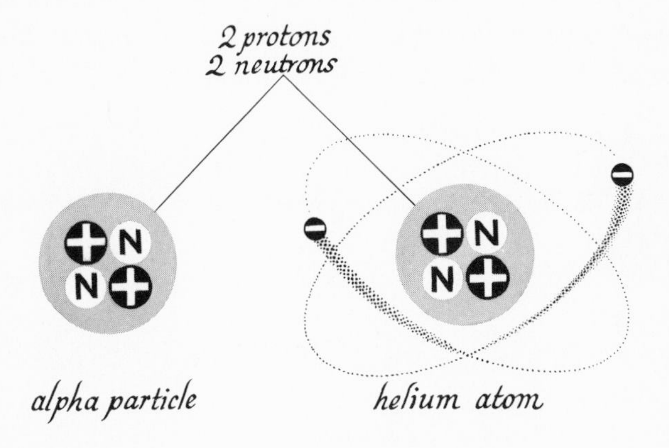


An alpha particle is the nucleus of a helium atom.

Alpha rays are made up of little "packages," each with two neutrons and two protons in it. One of these "packages" is called an ALPHA PARTICLE. One disintegrating atom sends out just one alpha particle. Billions of atoms exploding in rapid succession cause an alpha ray.

An alpha particle is itself an atomic nucleus. There is but one element that has two protons and two neutrons in its atomic nucleus. It is helium, atomic no. 2. Alpha particles are helium atoms, shorn of their electrons. They are positively charged ions, just like any atom whose electrons have wandered away.

Beta rays are made up of electrons. Each electron in a beta ray is called a BETA PARTICLE. A beta ray is a stream of electrons. How can this be so if beta rays, like the other two rays, come from within the atomic nuclei? And if electrons whirl around outside the atomic nuclei? And if there are no electrons in an atomic nucleus, just protons and neutrons?

Here is the answer to this mystery. When a *beta-emitting* atom explodes, a neutron changes to a proton and an electron. The electron cannot stay in the nucleus. Oddly enough, it is too large. It shoots out—as one particle in a beta ray. The newly formed proton remains.

Both alpha and beta rays are made up of particles from the atomic nucleus.

GAMMA RAYS are not particles but *waves of energy* released when an atom disintegrates. Heat and light are also waves of energy —as are x-rays, which are used to locate a bone fracture or some foreign substance in the body. Gamma rays are similar to heat and light waves. They are exactly the same as x-rays though they are formed differently.

Alpha, beta, and gamma rays travel at great speeds. Gamma rays go at the speed of light—186,000 miles a second. They are the most powerful of the three rays. They can penetrate several inches of steel.

Some beta rays go almost as fast as gamma rays, but even in the air they can travel only a few feet. They can pierce up to two millimeters of lead or move a short ways through body tissue.

Alpha rays, compared with beta or gamma rays, crawl along like tortoises. They travel only about 12,000 miles a second. We say "only," although if they could keep going at this rate they would

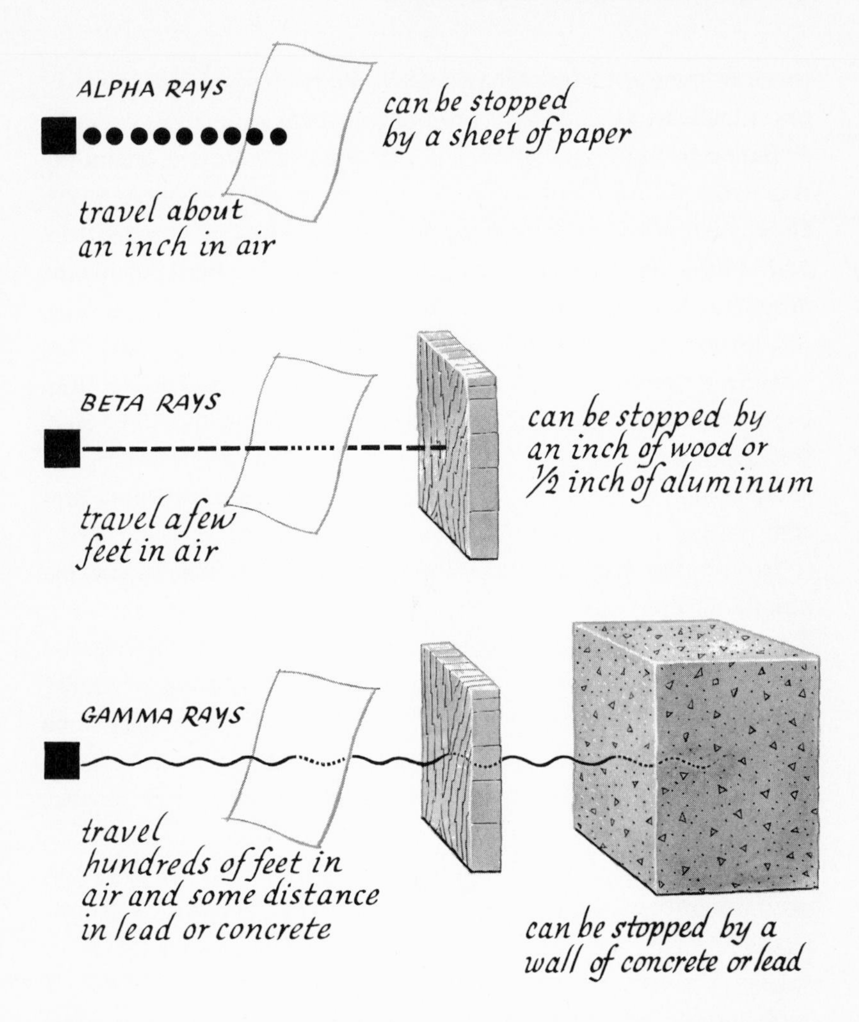


Three types of nuclear radiation—a comparison of their penetrative power.

reach the moon in less than 25 seconds. No earth-born alpha ray will ever reach the moon, for an air journey of about an inch exhausts alpha particles completely. They can push through an extremely thin sheet of aluminum or gold foil, but are stopped by ordinary paper. Compared with beta particles or electrons, they are heavy and clumsy. An alpha particle has a mass or weight almost 7,500 times that of a beta particle.

How does a scientist separate alpha, beta, and gamma rays? He places a speck of a radioactive substance in a lead container with a tiny hole at one end. The three rays shoot out of the hole in a single beam.

Next, he places a magnetic apparatus around the beam. The magnet causes the positively charged alpha particles to bend slightly in one direction and the negatively charged beta particles, which are lighter, to bend much further in the opposite direction. The gamma rays, being waves of energy, are not affected by the magnet. Instead of having the beam pass through a strong magnetic field, the scientist may have it pass through a strong electric field, as in the diagram on the opposite page.

This diagram of alpha, beta, and gamma rays is one of the first things nuclear science students learn. They make this joke about it: "Since alpha rays go to the left, beta rays to the right, and gamma rays straight up, the only safe place to stand is underneath the atom."

Don't try to take this joke literally. Any radioactive substance sends out its rays in all directions. In this experiment, all the rays are absorbed by the lead container except those which escape through the tiny opening.

Since alpha and beta rays are electrically charged, they add electrons to, or take electrons away from, the atoms and molecules through which they pass. In this way they leave a trail of negatively

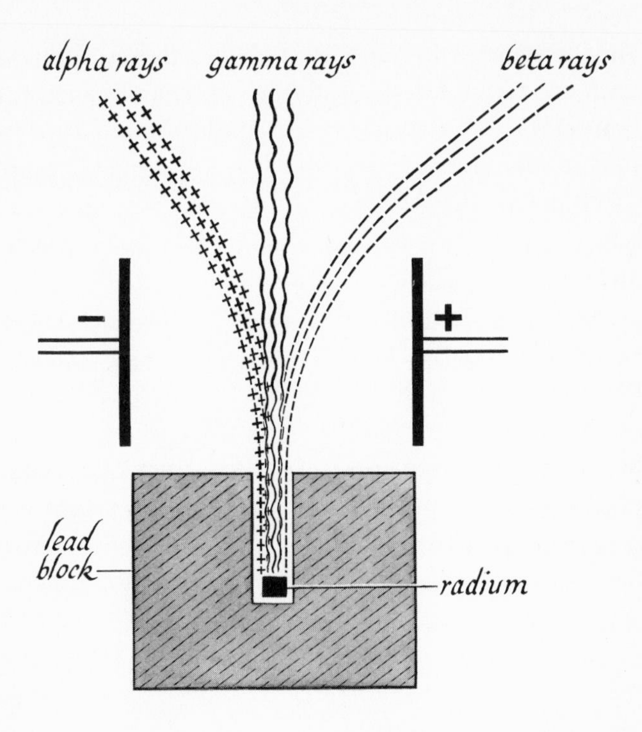


Separating the three types of rays that issue from radium. Lead is an absorber of this radiation—holds it like a sponge—and so the little hole provides an escape.

or positively charged atoms, or ION PAIRS. (One positively charged atom plus one negatively charged atom are called an ion pair.)

Alpha and beta rays are said to be IONIZING RADIATION, because they make ions. Gamma rays also cause ionization, indirectly. It is this ionization, or making of ion pairs, that causes a Geiger counter click. A sensitive counter can detect and record all degrees of ionization.

Radioactivity is measured by the number of ion pairs its rays make. The measurement is in terms of ROENTGENS, so called after William Roentgen, the discoverer of x-rays. One roentgen of radiation amounts to two billion ion pairs created in one cubic centimeter of dry air. The symbol of roentgen is "r."

Radioactive isotopes may shoot out all three rays—alpha, beta, and gamma—or just one or two of them. Only the heavier elements emit alpha particles. The three rays may be feeble or strong, depending on how fast the atoms are disintegrating, and on other factors.

In nature, there are 73 known radioactive isotopes. Each, even those of the same element, disintegrates at its own special rate. The time it takes for half the atoms of a radioactive isotope to disintegrate is called its HALF-LIFE.

Here is how a French mathematician, Emile Borel, explained this intriguing expression, half-life.

The time it takes for a certain amount of a radioactive isotope to decrease by one half through disintegration is called its half-life. Here are several stages of the half-life breakdown of Radium-226.

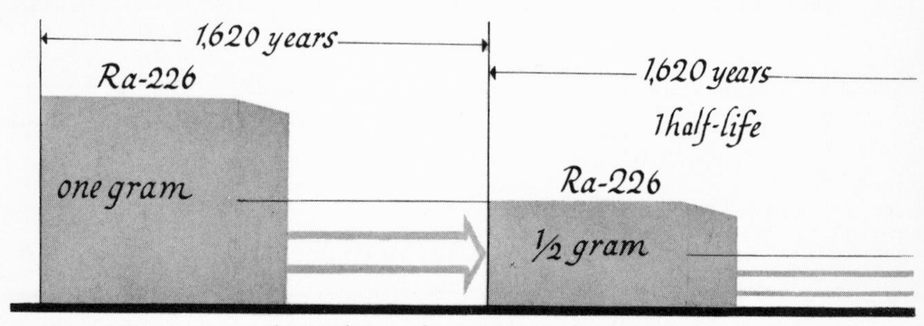


*half-life of radium · · 1,620 years*
*(rate of disintegration)*

Suppose a restaurant owner buys a supply of dishes for his restaurant. He knows these dishes won't last forever. Sooner or later accidents are bound to occur. He can estimate from previous experience that in six months, or a year, or two years, half these dishes will be broken. The time it takes for half of them to break is their half-life.

A scientist cannot tell *when* a particular atom is going to break down, any more than the restaurant owner knows which of his plates will break first. But, like the restaurant owner, the scientist can estimate how many atoms will disintegrate in a given time.

In one gram of Radium-226, some 37 billion atoms disintegrate every second. Though offhand this sounds like an enormous number of disintegrations, radium diminishes quite slowly. In 1,620 years half of the gram of radium will still be intact. The half-life of Radium-226 therefore is 1,620 years.

In another 1,620 years there will be only one quarter of a gram left. In another 1,620 years, it will be reduced to one-eighth. So it will continue down through the ages, until the very last atoms of that original gram have finally decayed.

The rate at which radioactive isotopes decay is measured in curies, so named after Marie Curie, who discovered radium and polonium. One curie is that quantity of any radioactive isotope

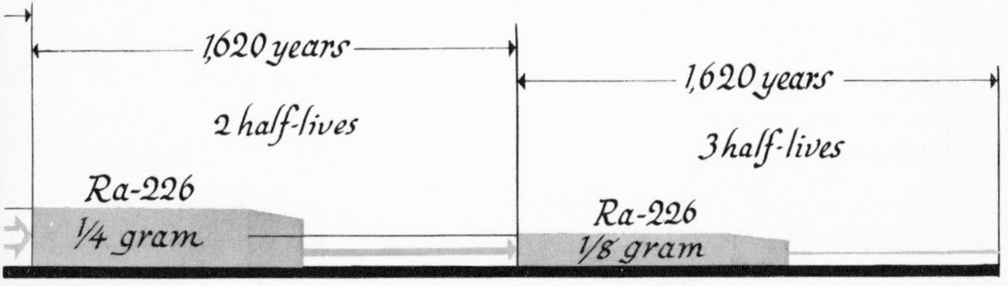


*half-life of radium··1,620 years*
*(rate of disintegration)*

which disintegrates at the rate of 37 billion atoms per second. One curie of radium is one gram.* Isotopes with longer half-lives than Radium-226 have fewer atomic disintegrations per second, so a curie of any of these is more than a gram. Isotopes with shorter half-lives than Radium-226 have more atomic disintegrations per second.

Uranium-238, atomic no. 92, is far less radioactive than Radium-226, atomic no. 88. Its half-life is 4.5 billion years. Its little sister, Uranium-235, has a half-life of 713 million years. Even these two have short half-lives compared with Rubidium-87, atomic no. 37, which diminishes to half only after 50 billion years. The half-life of some other radioactive isotopes, at the other extreme, is measured in microseconds, a microsecond being a millionth of a second. Such isotopes die so fast, it is almost as though they were never born.

## *Elements Can Change Into Other Elements*

What happens to an atom when it disintegrates? Does it just disappear? Not at all. It merely turns into an atom of another element. Radioactive elements, all by themselves, are constantly changing into other elements. That is the miracle of radioactivity.

Thorium-234, atomic no. 90, emits beta rays. To do this means that when one of its atoms disintegrates, a neutron changes to a proton and an electron. The electron shoots out but the proton remains. The atom now has one less neutron and one more proton in its nucleus. With 91 protons, the atom becomes atomic no. 91. It still has the same mass number, since it still has the same *total* of neutrons and protons. But it is now a new element: Protactinium-234.

* Curies and roentgens are the two terms of measurement for radioactive materials. Roentgens apply to the number of ion pairs that radioactive rays form. Curies apply to the rate of atomic disintegrations.

Thorium-234 and Protactinium-234 are called ISOBARS. Isobars are isotopes which have the same mass number and the same atomic weight, but which belong to different elements. The word has a Greek derivation: *iso,* meaning "same" (as in isotopes); and *baros,* meaning "weight."

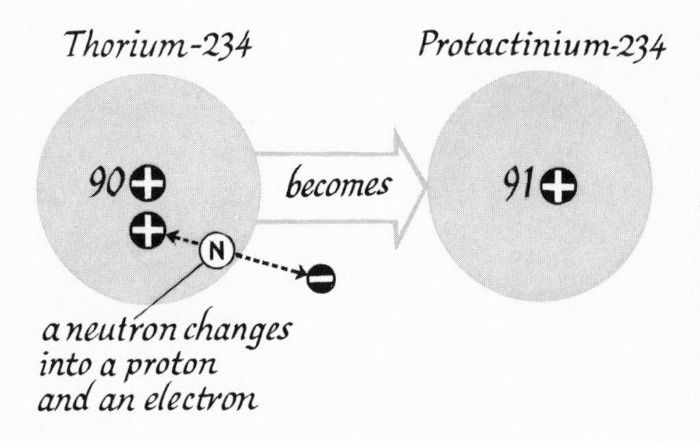


The tale of Thorium-234 changing into its isobar, Protactinium-234.

Radium-226, atomic no. 88, sends out alpha rays. Each disintegrating atom shoots out an alpha particle: two protons and two neutrons. Losing two protons, it becomes atomic no. 86, the element radon. (This is the only gas among the heavier elements.) Since this atom has lost four particles in all, its mass number is decreased by four. The new name for this isotope is Radon-222.

Different combinations are possible, depending on the type and number of rays emitted. All natural radioactive atoms turn into other atoms either one or two atomic numbers above or below the original atom.

Radon-222 may be called the child of Radium-226. Protactinium-234, atomic no. 91, is the child of Thorium-234, atomic no. 90. All four of these radioactive isotopes are descendants of Uranium-238, which is the patriarch of a huge isotope family. There are 17 descendants in all in the Uranium-238 family tree. The last of the list is Lead-206, which is stable and thus cannot have isotope children.

All Uranium-238 will, eventually, become stable Lead-206. But this process will take countless billions of years.

Uranium-235 has 15 isotope descendants, none the same as those of its sister, Uranium-238. The end of the U-235 family line is another stable lead isotope, Lead-207.

Lead-206 and Lead-207 are RADIOGENIC isotopes (—genic from *genesis*, "to be born"). They are stable and do not decay. As the disintegration of their uranium families continues, their amounts increase. Thus there is a building-up process in radioactivity as well as a decaying process.

All radioactive isotopes have family trees, some of one descendant, some of many.

In stable elements, isotopes are nearly always evenly mixed within their element. In these radioactive family trees, isotopes are

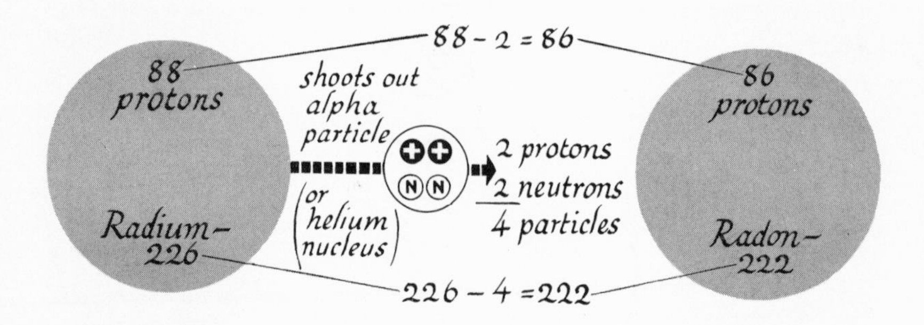


A disintegrating atom of Radium-226 becomes an atom of Radon-222.

ARGONNE NATIONAL LABORATORY

A nuclear scientist from Madrid and a student from Detroit, experimenting together in a laboratory session of the International School of Nuclear Science and Engineering, under the auspices of the Atoms for Peace Program.

often isolated from other isotopes of their element. This is not true of U-238 and U-235, which are found mixed in the proportions of 140 to 1. It is thought that when the world was new, there were equal amounts of these two isotopes. There are fewer U-235 atoms now because they disintegrate more rapidly than those of U-238.

All the radioactive substances we have discussed in this chapter exist in nature, and release radioactivity around us. It is in the ocean, in the earth, in the air we breathe, in the food we eat. It finds its way into the human body.

Every human being has nearly 400,000 atomic disintegrations each second. They come mostly from Carbon-14, Potassium-40, and tritium. This need worry no one. A single body cell, which is so little you have to use a microscope to see it, has an average of 90 trillion atoms. The disintegrating atoms in the human body are a very small drop in a big bucket. You don't hear, see, or feel these tiny disintegrations. Neither do you need to fear them.

The radioactivity all around us is called NATURAL BACKGROUND RADIOACTIVITY. So long as it is scattered over the globe, there is not enough to cause trouble. The human race has survived very well in spite of it.

Neither does this background radioactivity do us any known good. Radioactive isotopes were no noticeable help to the human race until man learned to make use of them.

*PART II*

# ISOTOPE MAKERS

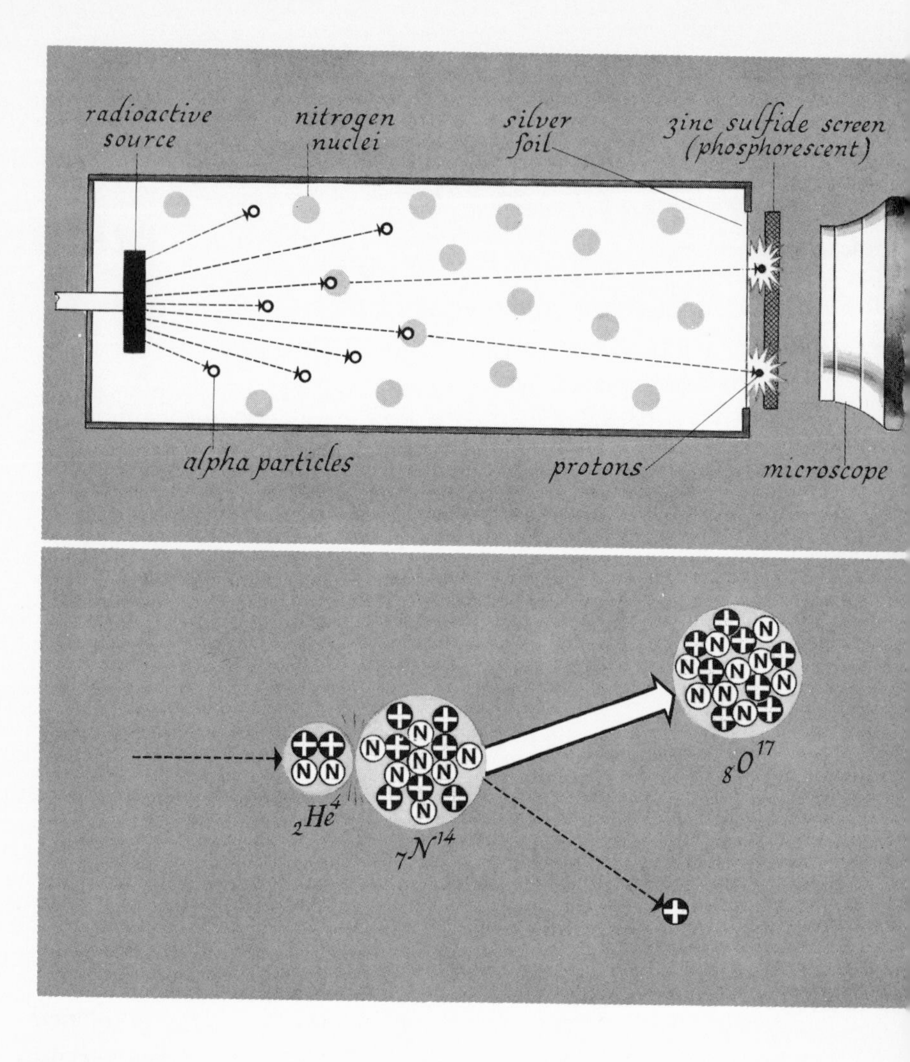


(above) Diagram of Rutherford's apparatus: a tiny nuclear shooting gallery, with a bit of radium for a "gun," some alpha particles for "bullets," and nitrogen nuclei for "targets."

(below) Schematic representation of what happened when Rutherford's "atomic gun" scored hits. He changed one element, nitrogen, into another element, oxygen. Nobody had ever performed such a feat before, though the old alchemists had tried for centuries.

# Man-Made Isotopes

## *Chapter* 4

IN 1919 a big, burly scientist named Ernest Rutherford was conducting a curious experiment in his laboratory at the University of Manchester, England.

For this experiment he used a short metal tube filled with nitrogen gas. In one end of the tube was a disk covered with a weak solution of radium. (Today the disk would be called a radium SOURCE.)

Rutherford's experiment was a strange form of target practice. In effect, the radium source was an "atomic gun." The "bullets" were alpha particles, and the "targets" were the nuclei of the nitrogen atoms. He was trying to hit the nucleus of a nitrogen atom with an alpha particle.

He had about as little chance, Albert Einstein said later, as of "shooting a bird on a dark night in a country where there are no birds."

In the vast empty space of the atom, the nucleus is the merest dot. Most of Rutherford's bullets went right through the nitrogen as though nothing were there. But since his atomic gun shot not one bullet but billions in a steady stream, eventually he scored a few direct hits. One out of about 700,000 of the alpha particles collided with a nitrogen nucleus. When this happened, the nitrogen nucleus shot out a proton, or hydrogen nucleus.

How did he know when this happened?

The far end of the tube was sealed with a metal sheet, thick enough to stop the alpha particles, but thin enough to let the protons pass through it. On the outside of the tube, just beyond the metal sheet, was a zinc sulfide screen. Zinc sulfide is phosphorescent. When rays or high energy particles hit a phosphorescent material, they cause a tiny flash, or scintillation. By counting the scintillations on the screen, Rutherford knew how many protons he had knocked out of the nitrogen nuclei with his alpha particle "bullets."

Let us explain the meaning of this target practice. An alpha particle (or helium nucleus) has four particles, two protons and two neutrons. Its hits were made on the isotope Nitrogen-14, atomic no. 7, which has seven protons and seven neutrons.

At each collision, the alpha particle made itself right at home—like a family of four moving in on a family of 14, making a total of 18. Only, the now-crowded nucleus did not have room for so many new members, and so one proton departed. The nucleus then had 17 atomic particles, of which eight were protons. The atomic number was increased by one. The new atom became that of a different element—not nitrogen but *oxygen*! Oxygen-17, with the atomic number of 8. Here is the formula for this atomic event:

Helium-4 + Nitrogen-14 → Oxygen-17 + one proton.

The changing of one element into another is called TRANSMUTATION.

Later the transmutation of a nitrogen atom into an oxygen atom was photographed. Does this seem incredible? It was done by means of a CLOUD CHAMBER. The main part of this apparatus is a glass vessel, the space inside saturated with moisture. Alpha or beta particles speeding through this vapor leave condensation trails behind them. Above the cloud chamber is a camera which photographs not the actual particle but the line of water droplets left in its wake. Experts by studying these trails, or tracks, can tell what kind of particle made them. Rutherford called the cloud chamber "the most original and wonderful invention in scientific history." The inventor was C. T. R. Wilson of the Cavendish Laboratory.

Ernest Rutherford soon became known as a modern alchemist. Though radioactivity had by now shown that nature could alter the elements, he was the first to realize that men could do so too. To be sure, he had not made gold. He had only changed a few nitrogen atoms to oxygen atoms. But he had paved the way for fu-

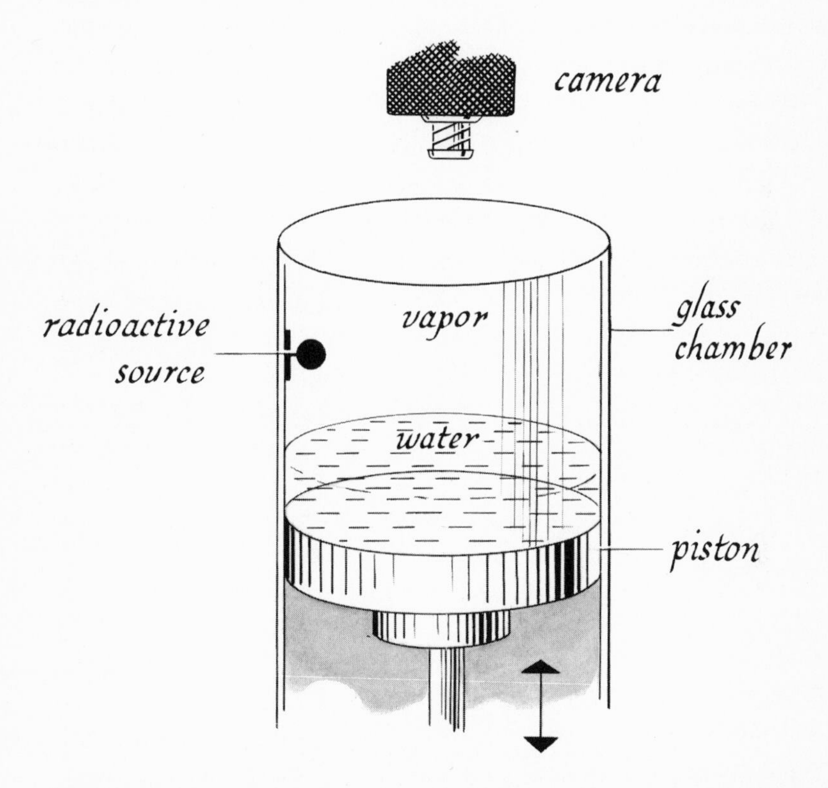


Cloud chamber. From the source, ionizing particles speed across the chamber. Their trails are ions and become visible when water droplets form in the same manner as on motes of dust in a cooled sky. In the chamber, the cooling results from suddenly expanding the air by a quick, short pull of the piston.

ture transmutations. Nowadays scientists know how to make (stable) gold from mercury. The difficulty is that it would cost several million times as much as to get gold out of mines.

In the next 15 years after Rutherford's experiment, other scientists, like magicians doing tricks they have learned from a master, made about 27 more transmutations. In all of these, stable isotopes of one element were changed to stable isotopes of another element.

In January 1934, science carried its mastery over matter one step further. Two young French scientists were making a nuclear experiment at the Institute of Radium, in Paris. They were Irène Curie (the daughter of Marie Curie) and her husband, Frédéric Joliot. Their atomic gun was a source of polonium—a radioactive element which Madame Curie had detected at the same time she discovered radium. For their target they were using a thin sheet of aluminum.

The purpose of their experiment was to make POSITRONS. A positron is an elusive subatomic particle which is exactly like an electron except that it has a positive charge instead of a negative one. It was first discovered in connection with the mysterious cosmic rays, those radiations which come to earth from outer space and are composed largely of extremely energetic protons. A positron is the most short-lived of particles—it lasts just one billionth of a second! Still, the Joliot-Curies with their sensitive Geiger counter were able to record that their experiment was a success and that their alpha particles, striking aluminum atoms, were producing the fleeting positron.

When they had finished their experiment, they sealed up their polonium source. To their surprise the Geiger counter kept on clicking. It did this for several minutes, quieting down gradually.

Untrained persons might have thought this an accident. The young couple, both carefully trained scientists, knew better. They looked at each other.

"I wonder if we have not created artificial radioactivity," Frédéric Joliot said to his wife.

This was just what they had done. From stable Aluminum-27, they had made Phosphorus-30, a radioactive isotope with a half-life of two minutes and thirty seconds.

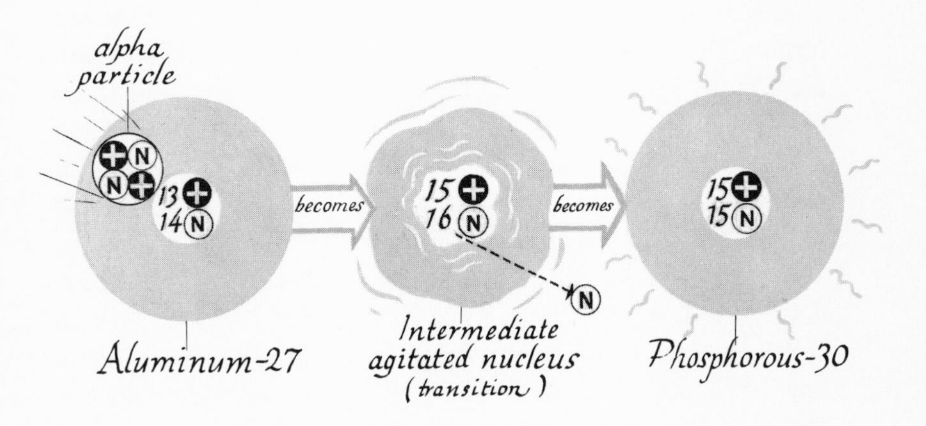


Formation of the first artificial radioactive isotope. A stable Aluminum-27 atom has 13 protons and 14 neutrons. It "swallows" an alpha particle, which is 2 protons and 2 neutrons. Then the intermediate nucleus is too heavy, and it tosses out a neutron. The atom now has 15 protons and 15 neutrons, and so is changed into an atom of the radioactive isotope Phosphorus-30.

The Joliot-Curies later confirmed the existence of Phosphorus-30 by a chemical analysis and recorded the atomic event with cloud chamber photographs. For their discovery of artificial radioactivity, they received the Nobel Prize in 1935.

The creation of artificial radioactivity was of enormous significance. Natural radioactivity exists in only a small proportion, compared with stable substances. A few natural radioactive elements, isolated from their surrounding minerals, had been put to useful work. Chief among these was radium. Radium was widely used in making luminescent watch dials. It was also used to treat cancer. It still is. It does not cure all kinds of cancer. Nothing does that. It does help in some cases.

Radium has several disadvantages. It is rare and expensive. Because of its long half-life of 1,620 years, it is particularly dangerous. If a minute speck of radium lands in the blood stream, it heads for the bones where, over a period of years, it may cause death. In 1924,

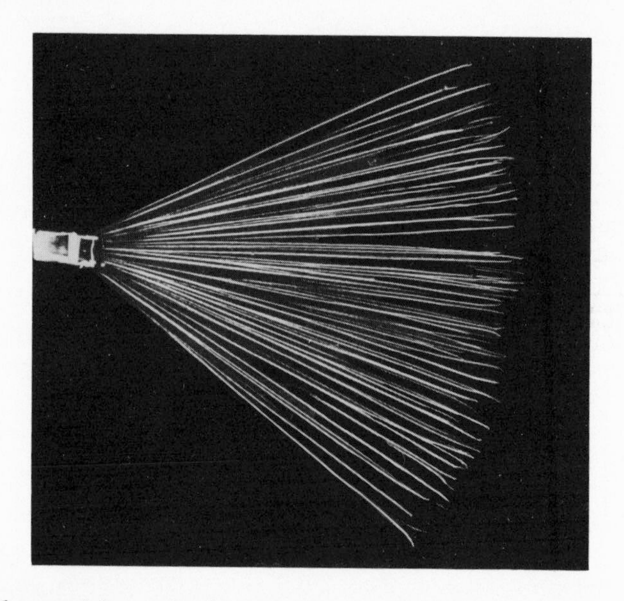

Alpha particle tracks in a cloud chamber. The source is at the left. After having gone some distance the particle slows down and is likely to collide with an atomic nucleus. This slowdown accounts for the bend at the end of some of the tracks.

before its properties were fully understood, a fearful tragedy took place at a radium watch dial factory in Orange, New Jersey. The 42 women employed there to paint the dials with a radium solution had the habit of smoothing out the ends of their brushes with their lips. The first of them died in 1925 of what was first diagnosed as anemia, but was later recognized to be radium poisoning. By 1958 all these women were dead from this same ailment.

There were accidents, too, in the first years radium was used for cancer. Though radium destroys cancerous cells faster than it does normal cells, some patients suffered severe radium burns because the safe dosage was not yet known.

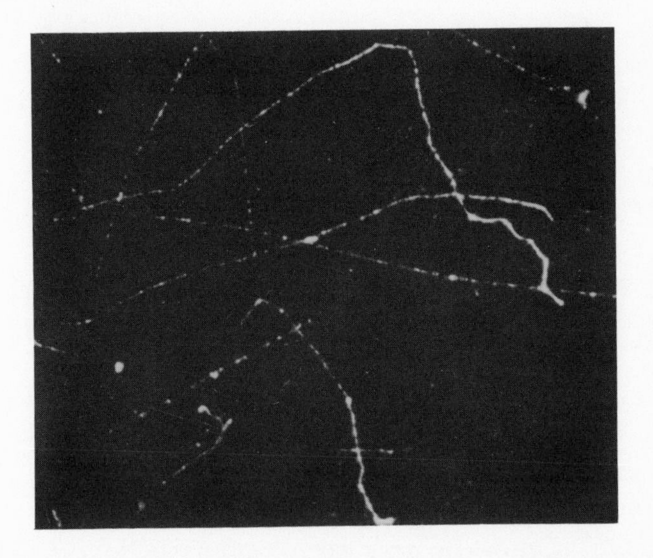

Beta particle tracks (entering from left). Note that these are straight only at first. As the beta particle slows down, its track bends more and more. This photograph and the one opposite were made by J. K. Bøggild of the University Institute of Theoretical Physics in Copenhagen, Denmark, and appeared in *Scientific American*.

After the Joliot-Curies made their artificial radioactive isotope, scientists began to speculate that isotopes which would be safer and more effective than radium for cancer and other purposes would one day be found, as later proved to be true. At the time it was only wishful thinking, for the few isotopes that could be produced in laboratory experimentation were insufficient for any practical purpose. So far, they were just a laboratory curiosity.

In Rome, an Italian physicist named Enrico Fermi decided he too would try to make some of the Joliot-Curie isotopes "just for fun." Instead of using alpha particles as "bullets," he used neutrons. Neutrons are better "bullets" than alpha particles, since they have no electric charge and so are not deflected by positively or negatively charged particles. (This advantage—as well as the fact that neutrons account for the existence of isotopes—makes the neutron one of the most important single particles in the known universe.) Fermi obtained his neutron source by mixing a speck of radium with a small quantity of beryllium, atomic no. 4. Within this mixture the alpha rays of radium bombarded beryllium atoms, which shot out neutrons.

At first he was unsuccessful with his neutron bombardments. His neutrons shot past their target just as a golf ball, if hit too hard, goes beyond the hole instead of falling in. Then he tried setting up a barrier of water or paraffin between "gun" and target. The hydrogen atoms in the water or paraffin effectively slowed down the neutrons. SLOW NEUTRONS hit more atom targets than do neutrons traveling at full speed.

With slow neutrons he made many radioactive isotopes of elements which in nature are not radioactive. Some had half-lives of from several days up to several years. The half-life of others was only a few minutes. To get them to the chemical laboratory for analysis before they disintegrated, he had to make a dash down the corridor from his own laboratory. Anyone who wanted to talk to him had to run along with him.

He had begun by bombarding the lightest elements, finally working up to uranium. Then something unexpected happened. Each U-235 nucleus that was hit by a neutron split in two parts. As we mentioned in Chapter 2, there is only one U-235 atom to some 140 other uranium atoms; so the atom-splitting could take place in only a small proportion of the uranium atoms. Fermi didn't at first know just *what* had taken place. (We shall soon show what happens in the splitting of an atom.)

He suspected, but could not prove, another interesting result of his bombardment. More plentiful than the atoms of U-235 are those of U-238. When an atom of U-238 is hit by a neutron, the neutron may lodge in the nucleus. As it does so, it changes to a proton and an electron. Then an electron—which may or may not be the one "made" from this neutron—shoots out, and the nucleus that has lost this electron is now left with an extra proton. Uranium's atomic number is 92, but the resulting new isotope has 93 protons and therefore is a new element. It does not exist in nature.

This man-made element is classed as a TRANSURANIUM element—*trans* meaning "over" or "beyond" in Latin. An element beyond uranium in the Periodic Table! Its atomic number is 93. It was appropriately named Neptunium for the planet Neptune, which is beyond Uranus (the planet for which uranium was named) in our solar system.

Here, expressed in the shorthand of physicists, is the whole affair:

$$ {}_{92}U^{238} + \text{a neutron} \rightarrow {}_{93}Np^{239} + \text{an electron.} $$

Neptunium was discovered in 1940, by two American scientists: Edwin M. McMillan and Philip H. Abelson. It was the first transuranium element to be identified. Others have since been created artificially up through atomic no. 103. All are radioactive. They are listed on page 174.

Some of these new elements are called "dinosaurs." Like dinosaurs, they may have existed on earth many millions of years ago and become extinct. Scientists believe they have found one part of Plutonium-239 to 10 trillion ($10^{13}$) parts of uranium in uranium

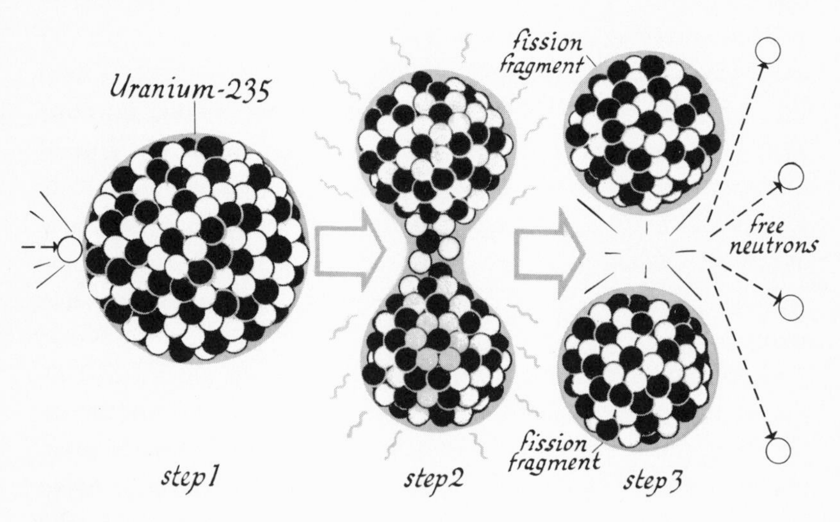


How an atom is "split."

ores. Pu-239 sends out alpha rays and has a half-life of 24,400 years. When enough of it was manufactured to be visible, it turned out to be a strange silver-colored metal. We will mention this isotope later.

Now let us return to the U-235 atoms, which, unlike the U-238 atoms, do not swallow the neutron shot at them but which "split."

Think of the Uranium-235 nucleus as a cluster of marbles imbedded in a ball of bread dough—92 red marbles for "protons," 143 blue ones for "neutrons." When a neutron shooting out from a source hits that ball, the ball elongates until it divides into two parts. This is what is meant by "splitting," or FISSIONING, the atom.

The two parts of a fissioned atom are FISSION FRAGMENTS. Each fission fragment contains both protons and neutrons, and is in itself an atomic nucleus. Not all the neutrons, though, fit into the atomic nuclei. Those that are left over are called FREE NEUTRONS. They no longer have an atom home. Fission fragments and free neutrons, alike, shoot out with great force.

The fission fragments may be any number of different atoms, and are always those of elements near the middle of the Periodic Table. For instance, they might be krypton, atomic no. 36, and barium, atomic no. 56. Add 36 and 56 together and you get 92, the atomic number of uranium. The atomic numbers of the fission fragments always add up to 92, to match the number of protons in uranium atoms. These fission fragments are radioactive isotopes; and sooner or later, depending on their half-lives, they disintegrate into other isotopes.

Of all the atomic events resulting from man's "tampering" with the elements, none created more of a sensation than the splitting of the atom, which Enrico Fermi and other scientists first did without realizing it.* The splitting of the atom was to lead to creating radioactive isotopes in quantity. Before this happened, however, the split atom would be responsible for the most terrible weapon of war ever known.

* Especially Otto Hahn and Fritz Strassman, two German scientists who, late in 1938, noted in their experiments that the nuclei of uranium changed by a surprising amount when they received a neutron "bullet."

# Isotopes in World War II

## *Chapter* 5

THE FIRST person to realize that the atom had been fissioned was Lise Meitner, an Austrian woman who because she was of Jewish descent, had fled from Berlin to Denmark to escape Nazi persecution. In February 1939, just before the outbreak of World War II, she published an article about the splitting of the atom, in *Nature,* a British journal of science. The article created the wildest excitement in scientific circles.

Why? Why was the fissioning of the atom more startling than removing or adding a proton or neutron in the atomic nucleus, which scientists had been doing for some years?

The reason for the excitement was that when an atom fissions, it transforms matter into energy on a scale previously thought impossible.

Matter can be transformed into energy? Does that idea strike you as new and strange? We mentioned before, perhaps so casually that it escaped your attention, that gamma rays released when radioactive atoms disintegrate are a form of energy. Gamma rays are proof that matter, under certain circumstances, can change into energy.

All radioactive substances give off a certain amount of energy. One of the first things discovered about radium was that it produces heat, a form of energy. In an hour a speck of radium produces enough heat to melt its own weight in ice. When Irène and Frédéric Joliot-Curie discovered artificial radioactivity, they also discovered nature's secret of changing matter to energy—albeit on a very minute scale.

In our larger world, matter and energy seem very distinct. To the casual observer what could be more different than a sunbeam and a table? Or the heat from a wood fire and a copper kettle? In the World of the Infinitely Small, matter and energy are not such separate and distinct things as they seem to us.

Light and other forms of rays are not a continuous stream, as once was thought, but are made up of tiny units, called QUANTA or PHOTONS. These small units have some of the characteristics of matter. Conversely, subatomic particles sometimes behave like waves of energy. The nearly weightless electron hovers on the very borderline of matter and non-matter. Sir James Jeans, a noted scientist, once said: "It is as useless to discuss how much room an electron takes up as to discuss how much room a fear, an anxiety, or an uncertainty takes up."

For decades theoretical physicists—physicists who deal with theories and mathematical calculations more than with laboratory experiments—have speculated on matter-energy relationships. They still do not have all the answers.

How much energy is there in matter?

This question was answered long ago, and very specifically. In 1905, the great physicist Albert Einstein, who was then only 26 and working as a clerk in a patent office in Berne, published a scientific paper containing a simple equation:

$$E = MC^2$$

E stands for Energy.
M stands for Mass (mass being a quantity of matter).
C stands for the velocity of light, 186,000 miles per second.

This equation says that energy is equal to mass multiplied by the velocity of light, squared. Not only are matter and energy the same thing in different forms. In matter—solid, liquid, or gas—lurks an amount of energy so vast it staggers the imagination. By this equation, one pound of matter amounts roughly to the energy from burning 1,500,000 tons of coal!

This is the most famous equation in the world.

Though Einstein's mathematical calculations gave absolute proof of his equation, he did not say how the transformation of matter into energy could be made. He did not know, nor did he then think it could be done on any scale larger than in nature's process of radioactivity. Hardly anyone else did either. That is why the splitting of the atom took the whole scientific world by surprise.

When an atom fissions, it releases some 200 million electron volts. Of this figure we can only say that while it is a very small percent of the total energy latent in the atom, it is many many times more than that released in the process of radioactivity. Atomic fission meant that mankind could create energy on an enormous scale —energy which could be used either to benefit the human race or destroy it.

Before this discovery could be put to practical purposes, there was still much to do. The first step was to find a way whereby atoms would fission in larger quantities than was possible in simple laboratory experiments. The solution was in setting up a NUCLEAR CHAIN REACTION.

We mentioned that a few free neutrons are released every time an atom of U-235 fissions. Within the mass of uranium a proportion of these neutrons, traveling at high speeds, collide with other U-235 atoms, causing *them* to fission. If each of two neutrons that have shot out of an atom splits one more atom, the progression mounts like this:

1 2 4 8 16 32 64 128 256 512 1024 2048 4096 8192

Since the neutrons travel very fast, each step of this progression takes place a million times in a fraction of a second. This is chain reaction.

The first theoretical proof of a neutron chain reaction was made in Paris by Frédéric Joliot and his scientific colleagues late in 1939.

Up until this time, nuclear scientists all over the world published papers on all their experiments. Nuclear science was a cooperative project in which everyone learned from everyone else. The splitting of the atom and the possibility of a chain reaction were news even for nonscientists. Articles were published in newspapers and popular magazines about these discoveries. It was prophesied that in the near future, light and heat and power would all be supplied by atomic energy.

Such prophesies were made too soon. In Europe, the Nazis were invading one country after another, plundering and killing as they advanced. Anti-Nazi scientists by mutual agreement decided to say no more about the enormous energy latent in the atom. No one knew what was in Hitler's mind. If he was thinking in terms of atomic weapons to enslave or kill the peoples of the world, no anti-

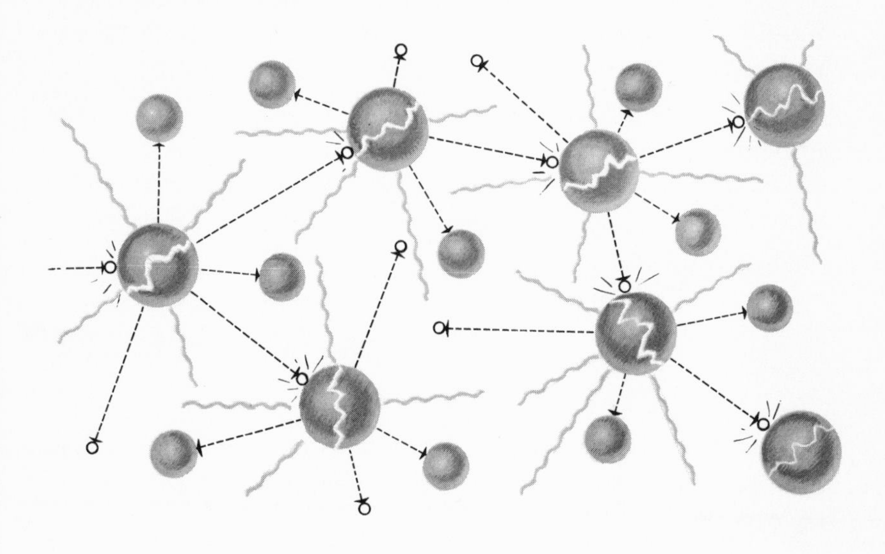

Nazi scientist wanted to give him any indirect help. In America the subject of atomic energy became "top secret" and remained so until nearly the end of the long war.

MEANTIME, the isotope, heavy hydrogen, rose to prominence in the war years. The Norsk hydroelectric factory in Norway had perfected a method of isolating heavy water (with heavy hydrogen in its molecules) from ordinary water. They were producing about a pound of heavy water a day. Compared with the minute drops

Ignited matches can be dangerous—or safe. Likewise fissioned atoms.

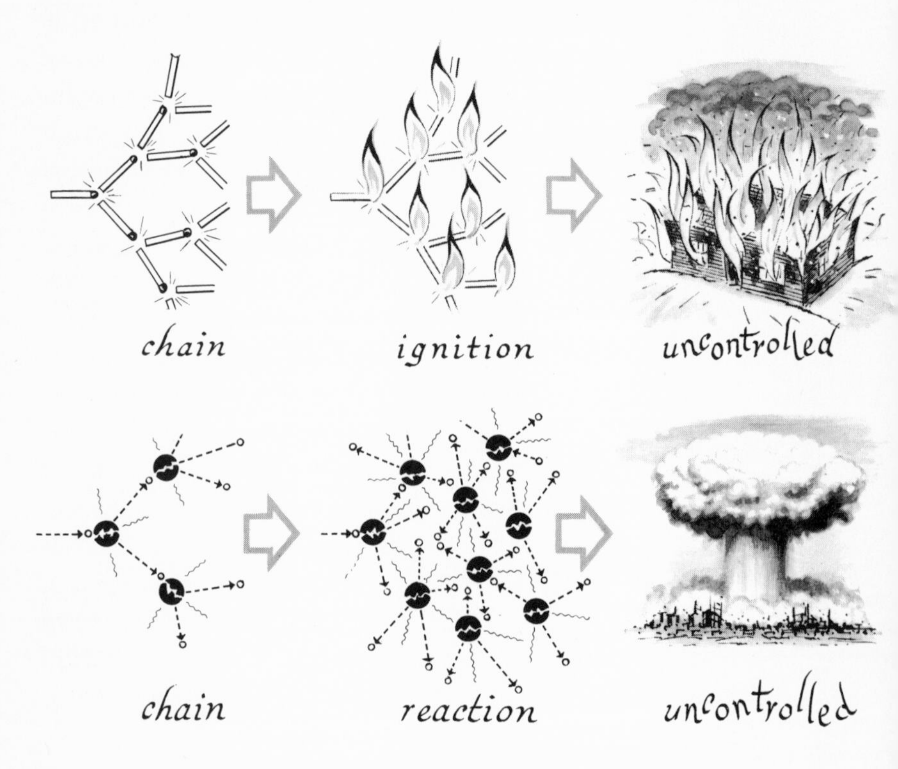

which could be isolated in laboratory experiments, this amount was huge.

Just before the war, the French government had bought the Norwegian factory's entire supply—about 40 gallons. This was nearly all the heavy water in the world. It was turned over to the College de France laboratory, where Frédéric Joliot and his colleagues were working on a neutron chain reaction. The French scientists wanted the heavy water to slow down free neutrons released in atomic fission. (The technical purpose of slowdown will be explained in the next chapter.) They found that heavy water was even more effective for this purpose than ordinary water or paraffin which Fermi had used in his neutron bombardments.

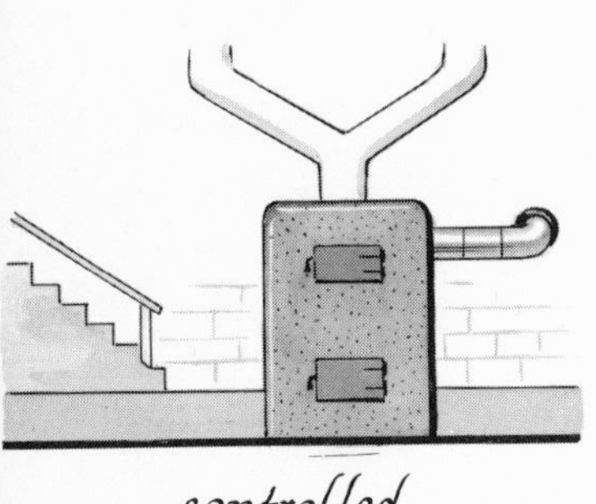

controlled

controlled

The Nazis invaded Paris in May 1940. They knew of the French purchase of heavy water and they wanted to confiscate it. But the water was not in Paris. It had been taken to the unoccupied zone of France, in Clermont-Ferrand. There it was stored in the underground vaults of a bank, in containers marked "Product Z."

With the Nazis taking over all of France, it was not safe to leave the water there. One night two French scientists and a government official came to take it out of the country. They traveled south with their cumbersome cargo, over roads packed with refugees. Every moment of their journey was dangerous. One night they hid Product Z in the death cell of a prison. The condemned prisoners carried the containers inside. The next morning the prison warden, afraid of Nazi revenge, refused to release the water. A drawn revolver made him change his mind.

After a series of adventures, the men arrived in Bordeaux on the Atlantic coast, their 40 gallons of heavy water still intact. An English ship named *Broompark* was waiting to take the water and scientists to England. Even then they were not safe. Through spies, the Nazis had learned where they were. But there were three ships leaving Bordeaux that day and the Nazis did not know which was to carry the heavy water. They sank two of the ships but the *Broompark* escaped them. The heavy water, and the skills of the two brave French scientists, were used for important research for the Allies throughout the war years.

This was the beginning of the drama of heavy water.

The factory in Norway was now under the Nazis. Word reached British Intelligence that the Germans had forced the factory to increase its heavy water production to 3,000 pounds a year. The Allies put the factory on their list as an important military objective.

A commando force of Norwegians parachuted to the mountains near the factory in October, 1942. They spent the winter learning every detail of its operations, how many guards there were and when they changed patrol, the position of every door, window, and piece of machinery. In February, with members of an English task force, they scaled the steep cliff behind the factory, entered it through a cable tunnel, set demolition fuses, and departed without a casualty. That night 3,000 pounds of heavy water were blasted from their containers.

The factory continued its operations. A few months later the Eighth U. S. Power Force dropped bombs in a direct hit. More heavy water was blown up. Discouraged, the Germans ordered the heavy water installations to be dismantled and sent into Germany. The Norwegian underground kept track of their movements. On February 10, 1944, a ferry boat en route to Hamburg was mysteriously sunk. With it went the installations and 3,600 more pounds of heavy water. That was the end of the Germans' heavy-water business.

One other war incident involved this isotope. Niels Bohr, a Danish scientist, was caught in Copenhagen when the Nazis invaded his country.

The Nazis let him continue work in his laboratory but watched him closely. He had about a pint of heavy water which he kept in his refrigerator in a beer bottle.

In the fall of 1943, Bohr received word he was needed in America. The Danish Underground smuggled him out in a fishing boat. He took with him only the beer bottle. On his arrival in England the first thing he did was to see if the bottle's contents were intact. They were. The trouble was he had brought the wrong bottle. The one he had guarded so carefully contained beer!

Later, Danish patriots, at the risk of their lives, rescued the real heavy-water bottle from Bohr's Copenhagen laboratory.

Thus did an isotope of hydrogen, differing from its brother hydrogen atoms only in that it has a neutron in its nucleus, become an international incident. Afterwards the Allies learned that scientists within Nazi Germany were using heavy water in neutron bombardment experiments, but that they never achieved a workable model of a neutron chain reaction, nor worked out plans for utilizing atomic energy for bombs or anything else.

Niels Bohr was one of several European nuclear scientists who found a welcome in America during the war. Another was the Italian, Enrico Fermi. In the United States, European and American scientists were working at the biggest and best kept secret in

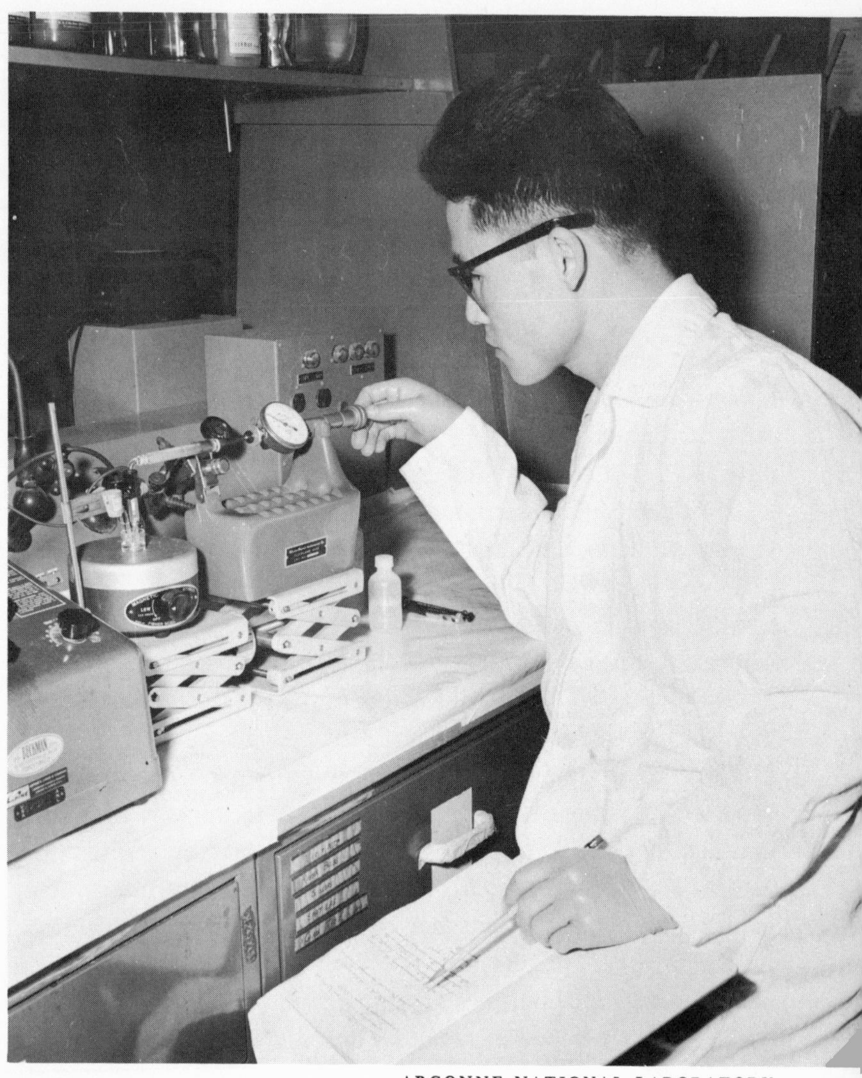

ARGONNE NATIONAL LABORATORY

Young scientist from the Republic of Korea, using a micropipette in a laboratory study under auspices of the Atoms for Peace Program.

world history. One of their many tasks was to devise a method of isolating Uranium-235 from its fellow uranium isotopes. Their secret became public on August 6, 1945, when an atom bomb (more correctly, a *nuclear* bomb) exploded over the Japanese town of Hiroshima. In a few seconds it destroyed a city, killed some 60,000 persons, wounded or burned 100,000 more.

This first nuclear bomb used in war was about ten feet long and five feet in diameter. It weighed 9,000 pounds. Its cost was around two billion dollars. Its power came from a chunk of hard white metal no bigger than a teacup—pure U-235.

On August 9, a second nuclear bomb exploded over Nagasaki, another Japanese town. The fuel of this second bomb was Plutonium-239, an isotope of the transuranic element, plutonium, atomic no. 94.

Five days later, on August 14, the Japanese surrendered. The United States won its war against Japan, so some claim, with U-235 and Pu-239.

The cost in human life was great. Many persons, not wounded by the actual explosions, suffered aftereffects from radiation poisoning. Some died within a few weeks. Others lived on for years before they succumbed to the damage which radiation caused to body tissue and bone.

When a nuclear bomb explodes it releases RADIOACTIVE FALLOUT, which is made up of fission fragments, radioactive isotopes formed by the splitting of the atoms. These isotopes come from many elements. Some have a brief half-life of a few seconds. Some, like Strontium-90, with a half-life of 28 years, and Cesium-137, with a half-life of 30 years, will still be powerful a century from now. Many have families of descendants which are also radioactive. Free neutrons, turning atoms of the air radioactive, add to the fallout.

If the bomb explosion does not go up above the troposphere, a portion of this mass of isotopes descends to the earth at once. This is LOCAL FALLOUT. Because of local fallout it is not safe to walk through a region where a nuclear bomb has exploded until tests show that radioactivity has died out.

If the bomb is big enough to reach as high as the stratosphere, the major part of radioactive fallout remains up there for some time, and is blown over much of the world. Later it is brought to the earth by rain or snow, where it increases natural background radioactivity. Tests of its effect, to date, are still inconclusive. There is no doubt about the devastation it could cause in an all-out nuclear war.

Since World War II, nuclear bombs a thousand times more powerful than those of Hiroshima and Nagasaki have been constructed. The world's "atomic stockpile" is now great enough to wipe out all the major cities of the earth, even without the aid of radioactive fallout. The threat of a nuclear war hangs over the world.

War has always been a fearful thing, bringing misery to innocent victims. If the human race is to survive, there can be no war which employs the incredible energy hidden in the tiny atomic nucleus. Young people today are growing up in the shadow of the dreadful menace of such a war. Unfair as it seems, this shadow is their inheritance. On the sanity and wisdom with which youth faces the problem, the world's future depends.

Atoms for peace! This is a slogan that reverberates more and more loudly. Happily, it is more than a slogan. In the fast growing Atoms for Peace Program, isotopes are coming into their own.

# Isotopes Unlimited

## *Chapter* 6

ON AUGUST 2, 1946, a year after the first nuclear bomb fell on Hiroshima, the Oak Ridge Laboratory in Oak Ridge, Tennessee, shipped a small amount of radioactive Carbon-14 to the Barnard Free Skin and Cancer Hospital in St. Louis. This was the first shipment of a radioactive isotope under the newly formed Isotope Branch of the United States Atomic Energy Commission.

Oak Ridge has since made many thousand isotope shipments. They go to hospitals, universities, research laboratories, and private industry in the U. S. They have been exported to about 57 foreign countries. Oak Ridge is the largest isotope distributor in the U. S., but isotopes are now manufactured in many other places, here and abroad.

As you have seen, all atoms, natural or man-made, stable or radioactive, belong to one isotope or another. Nowadays the word "isotope" is often used to mean either the stable or the radioactive kind. It appears as a general term in some official titles; thus the Isotope Branch of the Atomic Energy Commission is responsible for the production, development, and shipment of both stable and radioactive isotopes—but far more of the latter. When it is necessary to be precise, science has a new word, RADIOISOTOPES, to replace the cumbersome phrase, "artificial radioactive isotopes."

Sometimes the word "radio" is prefixed to a special element which has been made radioactive, such as radiogold, radioiodine, radiophosphorus, and so forth.

Radioisotopes are commonly measured in curies. For those with short half-lives, a curie is very little indeed. A curie of radiophosphorus weighs only about 1/10,000,000 of an ounce. A millicurie

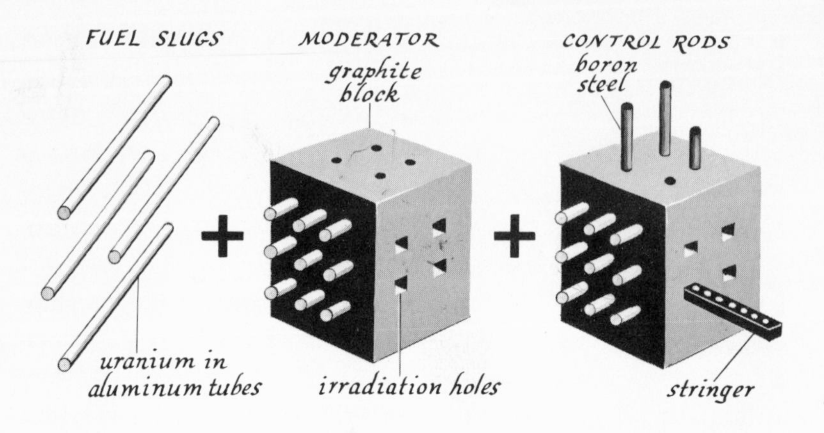


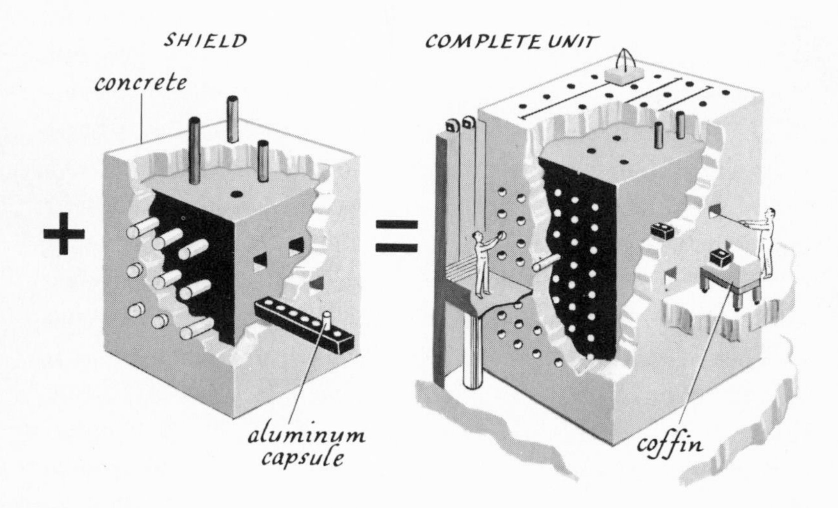


The make-up of a nuclear reactor.

is a thousandth of a curie and a microcurie is a millionth of a curie. Prices for radioisotopes, set in millicuries, are continually being revised downward as techniques for producing them improve. These prices have little relation to the prices of the same substances in stable forms.

How are radioisotopes manufactured? Most are made in NUCLEAR REACTORS.

A nuclear reactor is a sort of atomic furnace. Like a nuclear bomb, its power comes from energy released when atoms fission in a chain reaction. The name "reactor" comes from "chain *reaction*." In a reactor, neutrons fission atoms at a controlled rate of speed and do not cause an explosion. The basic principle of a nuclear reactor is its *controlled chain reaction*.

The first nuclear reactor, then called an "atomic pile," was constructed in November, 1942, under the supervision of Enrico Fermi, beneath the west stand of Staggs Field, at the University of Chicago. No newspapers reported this important event, for it was part of the Government's top-secret war effort.

There are many kinds of nuclear reactors, large and comparatively small. Some are used almost solely for producing isotopes, and these are generally spoken of as RESEARCH REACTORS. Others are spoken of as POWER REACTORS because they produce energy in the form of heat which makes steam for turbines in the generating of electricity. These reactors also supply heat for the mechanical power of ships and submarines.

What does it look like, this strange machine that makes tremendous energy from incredibly small amounts of matter?

One type of research reactor is a rectangular structure about 50 feet high, 40 feet long, and 35 feet wide. Its walls are concrete, some five feet thick. This is the reactor's SHIELD. It absorbs the deadly radiation from fissioning atoms so that they cannot reach anybody who is near the reactor. Within the shield is an empty space several feet wide, like a moat surrounding a castle. This space is further protection, since radiation decreases with distance.

The reactor proper is a lattice work or "pile" of graphite bricks. The graphite is the MODERATOR. It slows down neutrons so they will hit their target atoms instead of shooting past them. Some reactors use heavy water instead of graphite as a moderator.

The FUEL for the reactor is about 50 tons of natural uranium, made up in cylindrical slugs encased in aluminum and inserted between the graphite bricks. Some reactors use *enriched* uranium as fuel. Enriched uranium is uranium so treated it has a larger proportion of U-235 than normal uranium has.

CONTROL RODS are used to control the rate at which the atoms are fissioned. (They should not be confused with the moderator, which slows down the neutrons.) They are made of cadmium or boron, elements known as "neutron swallowers" because their atomic nuclei easily absorb free neutrons. If a neutron, so to speak, calls on atoms of cadmium or boron, he is received as one of the family. When all the control rods are inserted in the reactor, it stops completely. The insertion or removal of a single control rod decreases or increases the rate of atom fissioning.

The COOLANT reduces the intense heat caused by fissioning atoms. It can be air, drawn through canals within the reactor by huge fans, or gases such as helium, nitrogen, or carbon dioxide. Liquids circulated by a pump are also used as coolants.

The shield, moderator, fuel, control rods, and coolant are the main parts of the nuclear reactor. To function properly, all these parts are planned with the utmost precision. The skills of many types of workers are required for the reactor's construction: engineers, electricians, boilermakers, carpenters, as well as physicists and chemists. In completion, it is a triumph of man's ingenuity.

UNION CARBIDE CORPORATION

Loading face of a uranium-graphite reactor at Oak Ridge National Laboratory. The operators, using a lead shaft in one of its many openings, have inserted a slug of natural uranium and are positioning this in a fuel channel for the production of radioisotopes.

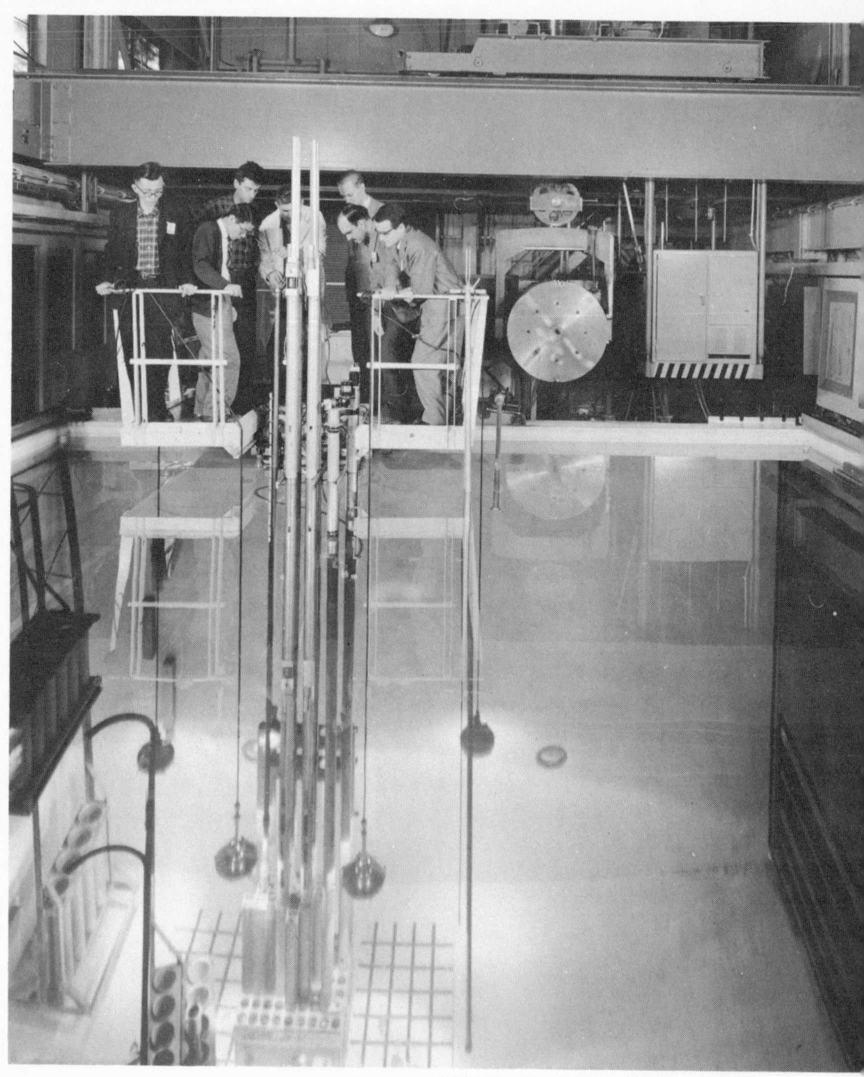

UNION CARBIDE CORPORATION

"Swimming-pool" reactor and students at the Oak Ridge National Laboratory.

How does it make radioisotopes? Insert any stable substance—a penny, a dime, a bobby pin, whatever—within the reactor, and it becomes radioactive. Neutron bombardment changes stable elements into radioactive ones.

In the base of the shield are openings, some like cabinet drawers, others like port holes. They are known as IRRADIATION HOLES and are usually kept sealed. When the reactor is not in operation technicians, dressed in white and wearing rubber gloves, wheel up a lead case known as a COFFIN. Inside the coffin is a STRINGER, a graphite block with openings to hold small aluminum capsules. The capsules contain stable substances to be made radioactive.

The technicians, using long tongs, open an irradiation hole, insert the stringer. Then, like bakers who have shoved bread into their oven to bake, they go off and let the neutrons do the rest. After a day or a week or a month, depending on the time specified, they will return to remove the stringer with its made-to-order radioisotopes and place it again in its lead coffin.

The SWIMMING POOL REACTOR makes use of a pool of water between 30 and 40 feet long, about half that much wide, and from 20 to 25 deep. The water serves as a moderator, a coolant, and as shielding. It is made as free of minerals as possible so that they will not take in the neutrons passing through the core. The result is that the water is even less radioactive than natural spring water. It is so clear that this kind of reactor has become especially helpful to students, because during experiments they can see core, rods, etc., in a way that would not be possible if the "works" were hidden under a great thickness of concrete shielding. This reactor does so many things that it has become a boon to advanced research, as well. Its technical name is BULK SHIELDING REACTOR.

As in a nuclear explosion, the fissioning atoms in a reactor produce fission fragments and the children and grandchildren of the fission fragments. In the reactor they are called RADIOACTIVE WASTE, which in its nature is similar to radioactive fallout.

Technicians periodically remove the used fuel elements containing radioactive waste from the reactor and transfer them to a deep indoor pool. As in fallout, some of this waste quickly decays to stable atoms. A large part of it remains radioactive for years. What is to be done with this dangerous material? That is one of the most serious problems in atomic energy development.

Various methods are used to dispose of this waste. Sometimes it is buried in tanks deep in the earth. Sometimes it is packed in concrete containers and lowered into the sea. A portion of the radioactive waste is treated so that it can serve useful purposes.

At the Oak Ridge Laboratory, the Fission Products Pilot Plant is devoted to the delicate work of separating the medley of isotopes in the waste. The process involves two major steps: first, to divide the isotopes into groups of similar elements, according to the intervals of the Periodic Table; second, to isolate these elements. The work is complicated and expensive. In one experiment more than 20,000 pounds of waste were processed to extract only 31.8 milligrams of radioiodine. One of the tasks of the next generation of nuclear physicists will be to simplify and perfect techniques for utilizing the steadily increasing stores of radioactive waste.

Radioisotopes can also be made by PARTICLE ACCELERATORS. Particle accelerators, as the name implies, are devices which speed up subatomic particles—protons, electrons, or DEUTERONS. Deuterons are the nuclei of heavy-hydrogen atoms. The acceleration is done by submitting a stream of particles to a heavy electric charge. A negative charge pulls the protons or deuterons forward because they are positively charged, and all unlike electric charges attract each other. A positive charge repels the protons and deuterons.

In some particle accelerators, these streams of particles travel in a spiral. In others they go in circles in a sort of atomic merry-go-round, held in orbit by magnets. An early model of particle accelerator was the CYCLOTRON, made in 1932 by Ernest O. Lawrence. It speeded up protons to an energy of 1,200,000 electron volts and was just 11 inches in diameter. Among other, later models is one with the formidable name of alternating gradient synchroton, at Brookhaven National Laboratories, on Long Island. It runs underground like a subway, has a circumference of half a mile, and is designed to accelerate protons to energies of 30 billion electron volts.

To make radioisotopes in particle accelerators, the technicians insert a stable element in the path of the speeding particles. This is the same principle as that which the early nuclear physicists used with their atomic guns. To compare the two devices, however, is to compare a 50-caliber machine gun with a .22 rifle.

Particle accelerators are fascinating devices and deserve a book to themselves. We pass over them briefly here because nowadays their main use is not to make radioisotopes but to do further exploration of the atom and its many subatomic particles, in addition to neutrons, protons, and electrons. The few isotopes manufactured in particle accelerators are those which for one reason or another cannot be produced in a reactor.

There is another way of manufacturing isotopes which will likely receive more and more attention in years to come. This is by a contained nuclear blast—an underground nuclear explosion contained in the cavity of its making.

Project Gnome conducts such blasts and is part of the U. S. Atomic Energy Commission's Plowshare Program. This program concentrates on methods of using nuclear explosions for peacetime purposes. Under the Plowshare Program, nuclear blasts enlarge ocean harbors and liquefy the petroleum frozen solid in the extreme cold of the Canadian Athabaska Oil Fields.

The first Project Gnome detonation was set off 1,200 feet underground in a salt formation 25 miles southeast of Carlsbad, New Mexico, on December 10, 1961. It created a cavity some 160 feet in height. Following the detonation, isotopes formed by the stream of neutrons from the nuclear reaction were gathered and sent to Oak Ridge and other laboratories for scientific analysis. Project Gnome also provides valuable data to the science of seismology, the study of earthquakes and similar phenomena, and is the basis for deciding whether nuclear underground blasts may prove a source of industrial steam.

WHEREVER there is radioactivity there is danger.

If you visit a nuclear reactor, you will see, near the irradiation holes and in other danger spots, signs such as the one in the photograph, opposite.

Such sections may be roped off for a distance of several feet. By the rope are pairs of big, heavy rubbers. A technician who must cross the rope slips his shoes into the rubbers so he will not track radioactive "dust" to other parts of the building. Should a scrap of paper blow inside this area, a worker picks it up with tongs and deposits it in a lead container marked "radioactive waste."

In atomic slang a HOT CELL is a heavily shielded room where highly radioactive material is processed. A technician who enters this hot cell, however briefly, wears a special type of "space" suit which radioactive particles cannot penetrate. For any experiment with strong gamma rays, researchers work behind heavy walls of lead or concrete, watching what is happening through a special kind of glass that is rich in lead content and about two feet or more thick. In such cases the scientist handles his material with ROBOT MA-

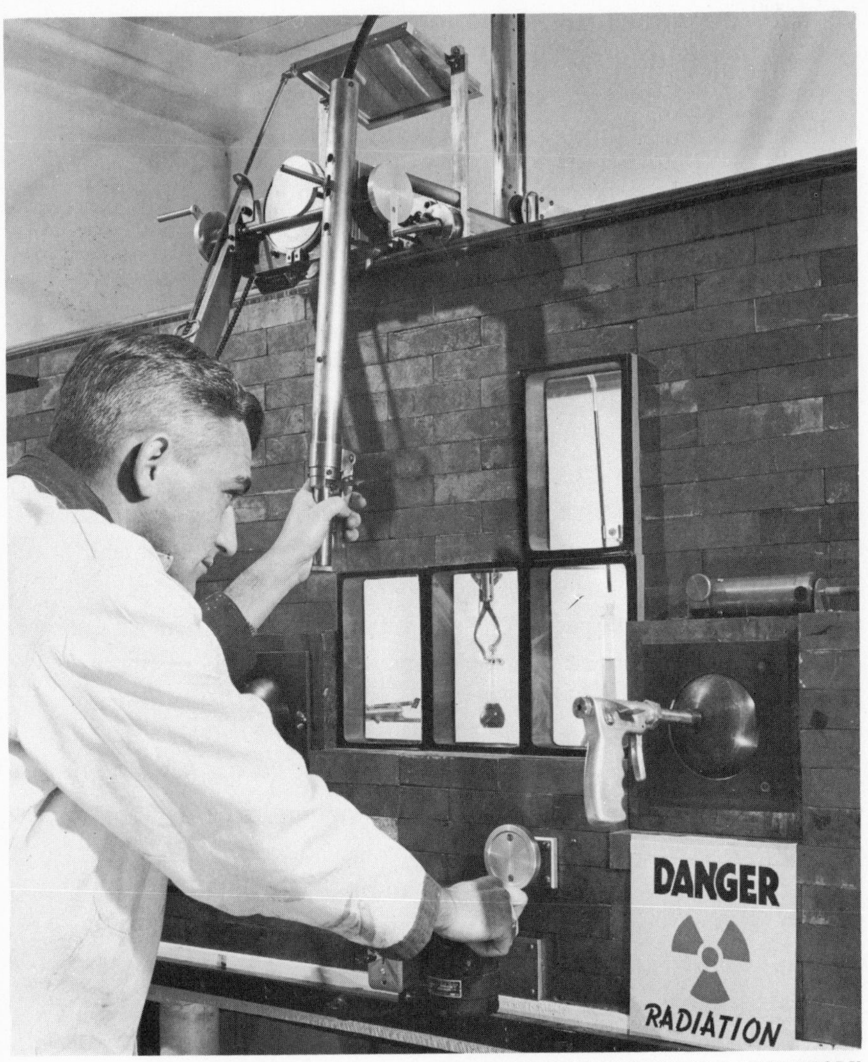


BROOKHAVEN NATIONAL LABORATORY

Handling radioactive materials with remote control manipulators, in a "hot laboratory."

NIPULATORS, which are almost as skillful as human hands for those trained to use them.

Stocks of radioisotopes are also kept behind concrete walls. In the "isotope store" the clerk never touches his wares. When he has an order to fill, his robot hands select the storage bottle and with a pipette pour the correct amount of solution into a smaller container.

Radioactive isotopes may be prepared as liquids, gases, or solids. Their shipment is a problem in itself. Those with short half-lives are sent by air so they won't lose too much of their activity before reaching their destination. Those requiring heavy lead shields go by rail express or motor freight. All radioactive materials are marked with special labels.

Shipping containers for radioisotopes weigh from one pound to four tons, depending on the radiation of the isotope. In one year Oak Ridge used a million pounds of shipping containers to shield less than an ounce of isotopes. Isotopes with strong gamma rays require heavy lead containers. For those emitting only low beta rays, a large cardboard carton, with partitions to hold the isotope bottle in the center, gives sufficient protection, since those rays go only a few inches through the air.

Though all procedures for making, handling, processing, and shipping radioisotopes have been installed with the highest emphasis on safety precautions, men and women who work with radioactive materials risk more exposure than other people. This is the first lesson they learn. It is not considered brave to take chances with radiation. It is considered stupid.

What is the threshold of safety? How much radiation can a human being stand? There is no definitive answer to this question. It is known that several small doses of radiation over a certain period cause less damage than one large one, since with smaller doses the body has time to make its own repairs. The Atomic En-

HANFORD ATOMIC PRODUCTS OPERATION

To cope with a spill of radioactive material, this kit is in readiness for AEC emergency teams to make quick trips to troubled places. It consists mainly of protective apparel, danger signs, maps and manuals, and instruments. Note small Geiger counter.

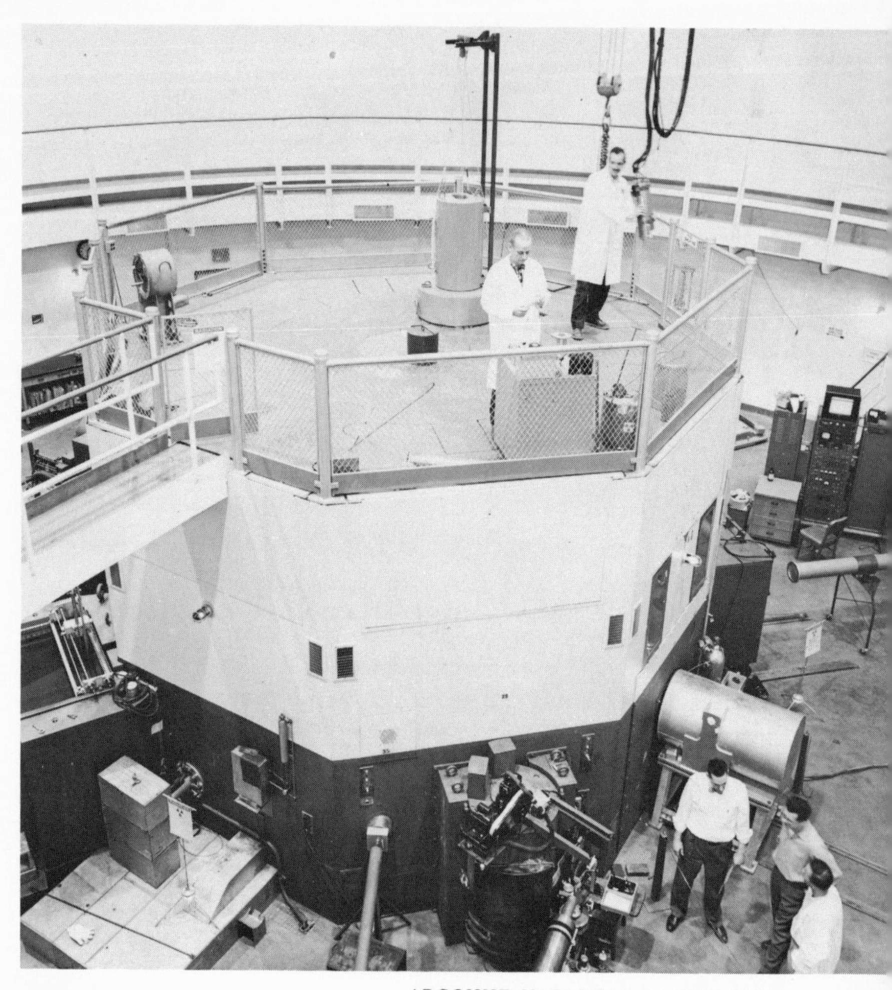

ARGONNE NATIONAL LABORATORY

CP-5, the Argonne research reactor, near Chicago. (The world's first nuclear reactor was "Chicago Pile, No. 1." See p. 77.) CP-5's whole purpose is to yield neutrons plentifully for science. Around it are instruments for various experiments. The one in the foreground is a "neutron diffraction spectrometer" for studying crystal structures.

ergy Commission sets a certain maximum radiation dose permissible for a certain period. If a worker says he is "all used up," he means he has had his maximum for the period and will spend the rest of his time in a nonradioactive area.

This "maximum permissible dose" is purposely set extremely low. Scientific studies report that an exposure of 25 roentgens has no detectable bad effects on the human system. A total body exposure of 100 roentgens in a short time would produce nausea, fatigue, and vomiting but permanent injury or death would be unlikely. A 250-roentgen exposure might mean death. A 1,000-roentgen exposure means almost certain death. No one should risk any unnecessary exposure. Even x-rays should not be made more frequently than the health of a patient requires. But panic and fear based on ignorance are not good either. Radioactivity has become part of our lives. It is important to learn how to live with it.

Employees in an atomic energy plant wear a FILM BADGE, a small rectangle containing unexposed photographic film, like that used by dentists for taking x-rays. Film badges are developed at definite periods—once a month or oftener, depending on the employee's exposure. If a badge should indicate undue radiation exposure, the employee who wore it is summoned for a physical examination, and if it is necessary he is hospitalized.

He may also carry in his pocket a DOSIMETER, which is usually shaped like a fountain pen and which will give a daily report of radiation exposure.

Special Geiger counters, resembling common scales, are scattered throughout the plant; on these the employee may make his own check on above-normal exposure on hands and feet. In the health department of the plant is a larger Geiger counter, which measures all-over body radiation.

The Department of Health Physics of the U. S. Atomic Energy

Commission has a staff of some 500 persons who study ways and means of preventing radiation exposure, the effects of such exposure, and proper treatment. No other industry devotes as much attention to the health of its employees. Because of the infinite pains that the Government has taken to protect life and health, the Atomic Energy Commission has achieved the highest safety record of any industry.

By nuclear reactors and other methods, over 1,000 radioisotopes have been made artificially. A few of these, like Carbon-14 and tritium, do exist in nature but in very small proportions. Of these 1,000 radioisotopes, about 150 are sold commercially and have been found to have valuable uses in science and industry. We shall now tell what some of these uses are.

*PART III*

# ISOTOPES IN ACTION

UNION CARBIDE CORPORATION

Hospital technician transferring Phosphorus-32 from a shipping container into a dosage bottle for treatment of leukemia and other blood diseases. Note pipette, tongs, film badge, etc.

# Exploring the Mystery of Life

## *Chapter 7*

BIOCHEMISTRY and biophysics are sciences devoted to the study of the chemical and physical nature of plant and animal life. Biochemists and biophysicists are men and women who are always asking, "Why?"

What, chemically, is taking place within the tubers of the potato plant, in the seeds of the pear, in a blade of wheat, or in the green bean as it forms? In what fashion is potassium used in the cells of yeast? How fast does blood flow? What are the inner workings of the liver, the pancreas, the heart, the brain?

No question is too farfetched to gain the attention of these scientists, so long as it concerns the hidden and enormously complicated processes that sustain life. Their aim is knowledge. If this knowledge has immediate practical value, so much the better. If not, knowledge is an end in itself.

The microscope was once their most valuable tool. Look through a microscope at a human hair, a bit of skin, a drop of water, and see for yourself its wonderful ability to make visible an invisible world. Delicate electron microscopes reveal not only the smallest forms of life but the giant molecules which are on the boundary line between living and inanimate matter.

But no microscope can follow the course of *atoms* as they flow in and out of living things, or tell how plants and animals make use of the elements they absorb in air and food. This is what TRACER isotopes are doing for the biochemists and biophysicists.

Tracers are usually radioisotopes which are mixed in minute proportions with stable isotopes of their element. (We say "usually" because in some instances *stable* isotopes are also used as tracers.)

Wherever stable atoms go, the tracers go too. A Geiger counter or some other instrument records their rays. Tracers are rather like the alarm clock which the crocodile swallowed in *Peter Pan*. They tell where the stable atoms are, just as the alarm clock told where the crocodile was.

If there is only one tracer isotope to a trillion stable ones, a sensitive Geiger counter will note its presence. A Geiger counter could detect an ounce of radioactive sugar mixed with two billion 100-pound sacks of ordinary stable sugar.

A few stable isotopes, like heavy hydrogen and Oxygen-18, also serve as tracers. Since they send out no rays, one must take a sampling of the substance they've penetrated and have it analyzed to learn their whereabouts. It is much quicker and more convenient to use radioactive tracers.

Tracers have various popular names. Sometimes they are called "spies," since they "spy" on the activities of stable atoms. Stable atoms to which tracers are added are called "tagged" atoms. The tracer is a tag or label to show where the stable atoms are. You can also say that tracers tag along with stable atoms. Compounds with tracers in their molecules are called labeled compounds. Biochemists and biophysicists call tracers "thinking atoms," because they sometimes seem almost human.

If you drink a glass of plain water, there is no way of knowing where in the labyrinth of veins and arteries and other body passages the water goes or how long it stays.

Suppose the water has a minute amount of tritium in its molecules, slightly above the proportion of one tritium isotope to a hundred billion other hydrogen atoms that exist in nature. Tritium, which has a half-life of 12 years, sends out weak beta rays. Follow these beta rays with a Geiger counter. The counter will report that the tritium—and therefore all the glass of water—quickly "gallops

BROOKHAVEN NATIONAL LABORATORY

Medical research uses radiocarbon to study the body's uptake, distribution, and excretion of sugars. After feeding a tagged sugar to a mouse, the biologist gets a sample of its exhalation on this disc. He then makes a radiation count.

off in all directions," becoming part of body fats, carbohydrates, and proteins. The body eliminates the water only a little at a time. In a couple of weeks half the water will be gone. It will take a month before the signals of the tritium fade away, showing that all, or most, of the original glass of water has left the body.

To demonstrate the use of tracers, lecturers on isotopes sometimes call on a human volunteer to drink a cup of salt water in which a minute amount of Radiosodium-24 is mixed with stable sodium in the salt molecules. The audience watches as the lecturer follows the tracer with a Geiger counter. Behold! The counter shows that in just 75 seconds some of the sodium comes to the skin's surface in the form of perspiration!

If the lecturer could continue his demonstrations over a period of weeks, he could show his audience some other amazing facts of sodium's journey. Some goes to the eyeballs and some joins up with the spinal fluid. Later a portion of it is absorbed in the bone structure and the teeth. Even in these seemingly permanent substances, it does not stay long. Between one and two weeks, half of the sodium atoms in the human body are replaced by other sodium atoms.

Tracers have produced irrefutable evidence that most elements we absorb in food and air and water stay but briefly. Half of the phosphorus atoms are replaced in a few weeks. Half of the carbon atoms are replaced in a month or two. However short their stay, all these atoms take an active role in the body's functioning. We are not like a locomotive which uses its fuel only to keep going. We use our fuel for continual and rapid replacement of all our body parts.

Iron is the only element that stays with us any length of time. We know about iron's sojourn in the human body from Iron-59, a tracer with a half-life of 45 days. As part of a red blood cell, iron atoms go to the spleen, the large gland near the intestines. There the cell disintegrates. The spleen retains the iron atoms in the discarded cell, as economically as a housewife who cuts off buttons from an old garment. From the spleen our iron travels to the liver, whence it goes on to the bone marrow where new red blood cells are made, with the iron as part of them. Then again the iron repeats its cycle, to the spleen where red blood cells are disintegrated, to the liver, and then to the bone marrow, only to start all over again.

With the exception of iron, all the atoms in the human being are different from those that were there the year before. He may look the same. He may think the same thoughts, remember the same poems, sing the same songs. But in physical composition he is not the same at all. Atoms flow in and out of living things as passengers pour in and out of a large railroad-station. This is one of the amazing truths about life which tracers have verified.

How does a hen make her egg? Tracers have been put to work on this long-perplexing problem, and we now know that both the yolk and white of the egg come, in part, from the chicken-feed the hen consumed at least a month before the egg was hatched.

How about the eggshell? Biochemists mix a few Calcium-45 atoms with stable calcium and serve it up with other morsels tasty to a hen's palate. Then they wait to see what happens. As though the radioactive atoms could speak, they report to various detecting instruments the tale of their adventures after they have been swallowed and digested.

They, and their fellow stable calcium atoms, are in a few hours absorbed in the blood stream of the veins. The blood stream carries them, like so many tiny fishes, to the heart. The heart is a meeting place for blood returning from many veins. Here the radioactive calcium atoms become mixed with all the calcium of the blood, a process known as DIFFUSION, and their signals become accordingly weaker.

The heart pumps the radioactive atoms into the arteries next, where they become even more widely scattered. Only a small proportion head directly to the oviduct, where the eggshells are formed. The majority go to other body organs, where they reside, doing their share of the work to be done there, until more calcium atoms come to replace them—like old tenants who stay on until new tenants move in.

This exchange of new calcium atoms for old ones is most marked in the hen's skeletal structure, which is largely made of calcium. Some atoms land in the tiny crystals on the surface of the bones, where they stay, as part of those crystals, for about two months. Others go deep into the bones, becoming part of them, for longer than two months. Eventually all are replaced. Over a period of months most of the radioactive calcium atoms reach the hen's oviduct, in company with at least part of their original stable calcium companions, and with other calcium atoms they have met in the course of their trip.

In the oviduct, they spend just 24 hours. In that brief time, radioactive and stable calcium atoms alike build what no modern engineer can surpass—the perfect oval of the eggshell, so fragile it cracks under the slightest pressure yet so sturdy it forms a safe refuge for a newly forming baby chick until it is ready to hatch.

Plant life, like animal life, reveals its secrets through tracers.

One of the greatest mysteries in nature is PHOTOSYNTHESIS, the method by which plants use the energy of sunlight to change water and carbon dioxide into sugar, fats, and starches—releasing fresh oxygen into the air. If it weren't for photosynthesis, animal life could not exist. All our food supply, directly or indirectly, depends on it. Our fruit and vegetables, the fodder for our cattle, even coal and petroleum, are products of photosynthesis. The air we breathe is replenished by the plants' gift of oxygen.

Photosynthesis has baffled science for over 200 years. Now bio-

BROOKHAVEN NATIONAL LABORATORY

A leaf from a plant that had been fed some phosphorus tagged with radioactive phosphorus. Researchers placed this leaf against photographic film, and the beta rays which the tag emitted from the veins of the leaf made this picture. It shows how much of the phosphorus fertilizer the plant took up and just where it used most of the food.

chemists have called on Carbon-14 and other isotopes to ferret out some of its secrets.

A simple water-plant belonging to the botanical group called algae is used for many such experiments. The biochemist grows the algae within a glass tube or other vessel, the air in which contains labeled carbon dioxide—that is, some of the molecules of the carbon dioxide contain artificially made Carbon-14. At various intervals, he tests samples of the plant by a detecting method called AUTORADIOGRAPHY.*

Place a radioactive leaf in contact with a photographic film and when the film is developed you will have a autoradiograph. It shows just where in the leaf the radioisotope is stationed. The tracer has actually taken a picture of itself.

Tracer experiments have shown the process of photosynthesis to be incredibly rapid. In six seconds the algae uses carbon dioxide to create more than twenty different compounds. In 60 to 90 seconds, carbon atoms are already incorporated in the complex sugar molecules.

Scientists the world over are carrying on similar experiments, and now and again one of them adds one more piece of information to the huge jigsaw puzzle of photosynthesis. There is still much to know. No one can say when or whether man will ever be able to master its secrets. If we should one day succeed in duplicating the magic which the simplest plant performs with such ease, it would be one of the biggest events of all time. Should we too learn how to make food out of sun and air, no one would ever go hungry again.

The study of photosynthesis is perhaps the most significant basic research problem which science has attacked with tracer isotopes. Biochemists and biophysicists have enlisted tracers for literally thousands of other experiments, most of a highly technical nature.

* Also called *radioautography*.

For some experiments, where no suitable radioactive tracer is available, the researchers use stable ones: Oxygen-18, Nitrogen-15, and Hydrogen-2 (deuterium). Even though stable tracers do not reveal their presence to the Geiger counter, science has special techniques for detecting them.

There are laboratory studies in which biologists substitute heavy hydrogen for ordinary hydrogen in bacteria, molds, and yeasts. The tests have shown that these double-weight hydrogen atoms actually slow down the rate of growth. Similarly, heavy hydrogen, when it replaces ordinary hydrogen in mice, slows the growth of tumors, a discovery which may provide clues for the war against cancer.

There is no sharp dividing line between basic research, with its emphasis on knowledge for the sake of knowledge, and the practical application of basic research. In the following chapters we shall refer back to the achievements of the men and women in white laboratory smocks as we see how their patient experiments have led to major discoveries for the health and welfare of mankind.

# Working on the Farm

## *Chapter* 8

THERE ARE nearly three billion people in the world. All of them must eat. The farmer supplies most of their food. In countries all over the world, isotopes are helping farmers in this mighty task. In the United States, the Department of Agriculture, collaborating with State experimental stations, carries on a wide variety of isotope research projects.

American farmers spend one and a quarter billion dollars a year, more or less, on fertilizer to make up soil deficiencies. The major portion goes for phosphate fertilizer, since many farm lands lack phosphorus.

How deep must it be spaded into the soil? How near the plants' roots? At what time of the year and at what stage of the plants' growth is the fertilizer most effective? The experts called on Phosphorus-32 to answer these questions. P-32 is made from stable P-31, in a nuclear reactor. It has a half-life of 14.3 days, neither too long nor too short for most tracer experiments. Of all radioisotopes, none is more widely used or for more purposes than P-32.

Agricultural experts, in their experiments on phosphate fertilizer, tagged the nonradioactive phosphorus atoms of the fertilizer with P-32. They used this tagged fertilizer on potatoes, corn, beans, cotton, peanuts, and other crops. Sometimes they sprinkled it on the soil, and sometimes spaded it in the ground at varied distances from the roots. Then over a period of weeks they tested the plants for radioactivity, with Geiger counters or by making autoradiographs. The presence of P-32 in the plant was proof that the fertilizer was being absorbed by the plant's roots. The amount of tracer showed how much of the fertilizer had been absorbed.

OAK RIDGE OPERATIONS OFFICE

Experiment with tomato plants to determine the uptake of strontium applied to the leaves. University of Tennessee-AEC Agricultural Research Program.

In the course of these experiments they discovered that some plants take up hardly any phosphorus through their roots, no matter where or when it was added to the soil. For these plants, the fertilizer was a complete loss! They tried using tagged phosphate fertilizer in liquid form on the same plants, applying it by sprays. They met with spectacular results. The plants drank in about 95 percent of the liquid phosphorus, through leaves, twigs, stems, and even flowers.

The discovery was a revolutionary one, for until a few years before that, liquid spray application, called "foliar feeding," had been still in the theoretical stage. Tests with other isotopes now showed that many plants can be fed most of the nutrients they need simply by spraying them. Citrus trees which lacked zinc and iron have been restored to health by being sprayed with solutions of the needed elements. Magnesium deficiency in celery was remedied by spraying, after giving the plants magnesium through the soil had failed.

By means of tracers farmers have learned that fruit trees will absorb zinc fertilizer through their leaves even in below-freezing temperature, that fertilizer for cotton plants is best introduced in the seeds at planting time, that clover assimilates fertilizer better when it is placed in holes dug in the ground than when it is spread over the field, and that sulfate fertilizer was in part wasted because certain soils would not assimilate sulfur.

If soil and moisture are right, why does a plant get sick, why do its leaves turn yellow, why doesn't it give a normal yield in fruit or vegetables?

It may be that the plant's sickness is due to lack of a MICRONUTRIENT in its nourishment. Micronutrient is the name given to certain elements present in plants or animals in such small amounts they are difficult to identify by chemical analysis. Tracer isotopes not only prove that these elements are present but find out how the plant uses them.

Soil fertility is a major subject for tracer investigation. Russian scientists, through radioisotopes, traced a sharp decline in clover to a lack of boron in the soil. In America, isotope tracers reported that a tomato crop was doing poorly because a rare element called molybdenum was blocking the iron intake in the leaves.

Why did fruit trees grown in the West, in soils with high calcium content starve for lack of iron—even when iron was added to the

OAK RIDGE OPERATIONS OFFICE

Preparing seeds for irradiation by a Cobalt-60 source, in an agricultural research project.

soil? Is there adequate potash in the soil in the Corn Belt? What was the reason for the decrease in the Burma rice crop? Tracers are supplying the answers to any number of such questions.

In the study of water resources, also, isotopes are advancing agricultural science. Radioisotope techniques are being used to measure the depth and density of mountain snow-packs so that farmers can know in advance how much water they will have available for the coming season. Tracers are used to study droughts, to measure depletion of water supplies through pumping, to check the effectiveness of the irrigation systems, such as those of Hawaiian sugar plantations.

Farmers must wage a constant battle against insects. California orange groves were threatened by tiny mites. Tinier tracers did research on insecticides to find one that would destroy the mites without hurting the trees or fruit. By labeling insecticides with phosphorus tracers, Southwestern agricultural experiment stations are perfecting more effective insect killers for use on cotton and other crops. Radiation from the isotopes that emit strong gamma rays is being used to destroy the pink boll weevil, the curse of Southern cotton plantations.

Over 300 million pounds of insecticides of toxic nature have been used each year in the United States. Unfortunately, powerful insecticides are poisonous to other creatures besides insects. In the past there have been many cases of arsenic or lead poisoning which could be traced to residues left on fruit and vegetables from insecticides. To try to overcome these hazards to health, the Food and Drug Administration has set up regulations to limit toxins to what is tolerable. Chemists and entomologists, working under the supervision of the Department of Agriculture, have the delicate task of determining the micro amounts of toxic residue on contaminated products, and of making recommendations on how to reduce such

BROOKHAVEN NATIONAL LABORATORY

In an experiment made by the University of Connecticut, gamma rays caused this white carnation plant to yield a red carnation.

residues and still give crops protection against insects. The accuracy and sensitivity of tracer techniques has enormously simplified their work. This is an example of how isotopes have served to increase public safety.

Tracer isotopes are investigators, not meddlers; they merely report on what they find. They do not change materials. But isotopes in concentrated form, particularly those with strong gamma rays, can cause drastic changes in materials, both organic and inorganic.

Gamma radiation is of special significance to agriculture because it can cause MUTATIONS. A mutation is a change in the basic features of a plant or animal, which may continue or reappear in succeeding generations. If a red carnation plant produces a white carnation, a mutation has occurred.

Natural mutations are very rare. Most mutations are bad—they result in inferior breeds which cannot survive. About one in a thousand mutations produces a breed that is in one way or another superior. Agriculturists are always on the lookout for good mutations. Finding one was formerly a hit-or-miss affair, as long as they had to depend wholly on nature. Now gamma radiation greatly betters their chances by increasing the mutation rate a hundredfold. Without this radiation, for example, only one kernel of corn in a thousand will show any mutation, good or bad. Radiation treatment increases this ratio to 100 mutations among 1,000 kernels.

One of the major projects at the Brookhaven National Laboratories, on Long Island, N. Y., has been a study of the effects of gamma rays on plant life. Picture a 10-acre field in a ring of oaks and pines a short distance from the laboratory buildings proper. This is a "gamma field." In the center of it stands a seven-foot iron pipe. It contains a slug of the gamma-emitting isotope Cobalt-60, and this source radiates 2,000 curies. That much radiation is equivalent to the strength of five pounds of radium. Not much more

BROOKHAVEN NATIONAL LABORATORY

"Gamma field" where experiments are made to study the effect of radiation on plants.

radium than this has been isolated in all the years since its discovery in 1898!

Gamma rays are much more powerful than alpha and beta rays, which penetrate only a few inches of air. The Cobalt-60 source is so strong that over the years it has killed the pine trees far out at the field's edge.

No one enters the gamma field unless the cobalt source is lowered into a lead container some 15 feet underground, which is done from a control shed well outside the field. The field is surrounded by a high wire fence and there is only one gate. Around and near the fence are signs warning of the danger of approaching too close.

Once, when the gamma field was new, the remote control system failed because the chain that should have let a slug of Cobalt-60 go down within the pipe to the underground container got stuck. To approach the pipe for correcting this trouble would have meant a lethal dose of radiation.

An expert sharpshooter from the Army was summoned. His orders were to race on the field, shoot at a distance of 200 yards, staying not more than three minutes. He had to hit the chain, not the pole next to it, which would have had catastrophic results for the entire vicinity. He did as he was told, fired once—and missed. He took a second shot and hit the chain. The slug sank into the ground as it was supposed to and the danger was over.

When the source is lowered, anyone can walk through the gamma field in perfect safety. Gamma rays are a product of radioactivity; they do not cause radioactivity. Twenty hours out of the day the Co-60 beams its gamma rays over the field. For the other four, farmers tend their crops there, like farmers anywhere.

Many different things are grown in this strange field—tomatoes, potatoes, tobacco, fruit trees. They are planted in circles around the cobalt source, at varying distances. The further away they are from the source the more normal they are in height and foliage. Those near to the source are stunted and straggly. Sometimes they develop weird tumors.

At Brookhaven is also a "gamma greenhouse." It looks much like any other, except for the tall lead pipe on one side. This is a Co-60 source of 15-curie strength, slightly over the radioactivity of a half ounce of radium. Potted plants are arranged around it in semicircles. Here, as in the gamma field, the plants close to the cobalt source are dwarfed and wretched, while the ones further away from the invisible rays are somewhere near normal.

By studying abnormal plant life, Brookhaven scientists find clues to help them understand the normal processes of plant life. Occasionally there is a mutation that looks promising. Brookhaven ships the mutated plant off to agricultural experts, who breed it through a number of generations to develop the superior trait.

Here are a few of the profitable mutations which have been produced by gamma radiation:

- a variety of corn which is resistant to leaf blight
- a navy bean bush, from a navy bean vine, which yields more beans per acre and resists fungus better than the original vine
- a peanut plant which gives 30 percent more yield than the parent plant and is highly resistant to leaf spot
- dwarf cereal grasses which suffer less damage from wind than their full-sized parents and also give a better yield
- a peach tree with fruit which ripens 10 days earlier than the usual variety, and another with peaches that ripen three weeks later than normal—so that the picking time for fresh peaches can be stretched out over a month.

Other mutations produced by gamma rays include wheat, barley,

UNION CARBIDE CORPORATION

Researcher using a counter to check on a radioisotope tag which was put into cattle feed during a nutrition study made by the University of Tennessee and the AEC.

mustard, soybeans with a higher yield, exceptionally large tomatoes, and cotton that produces a high yield in Texas, where cotton yield has been lower per acre than in other states.

More recently, work has begun on gamma-produced mutation of poultry.

Animal husbandry has also profited by isotope techniques. Use of tracers make possible more scientific feeding of our livestock. Scientific research men inject various labeled compounds into the fodder. With Geiger counters they gather evidence on which substances are quickly rejected and eliminated and which stay to become part of blood or tissue or bone. Once it was thought that lambs digested only about 20 percent of the phosphorus naturally present in alfalfa hay. A tracer study showed they digested up to 90 percent of the phosphorus, giving reassurance to sheep men that alfalfa hay is an excellent source of phosphorus for the flocks.

Scientists in Missouri have used radioiodine to learn which breeds of cattle can best stand heat. In Wyoming, they used radiosulfur to study cattle poisoning from selenium (atomic no. 34) an element resembling sulfur, which plants take up from the soil. Strontium-90, a gamma-emitting isotope, is used to treat eye and skin infections in cows, and elsewhere isotopes are gathering data on bloat, which has cost cattle breeders millions of dollars.

The dairy cow has been studied in tracer experiments down to the last enzyme and molecule. She is well worth all this isotope investigation. The Queen of Food Providers, she gives us milk, butter, cream, and cheese.

Livestock, like plants, require in their diet minute amounts of certain metallic elements such as copper, zinc, and cobalt. In animals, too, these are called micronutrients. As in plants, their amount in blood and tissue is too small for chemical analysis. Cobalt-60, Zinc-65, and Copper-64, when used as tracers, tell how much of a micronutrient the animals assimilate and to what use they put it. Cobalt-60, for instance, reports that cattle will literally starve to death unless they have four parts of cobalt to 100 million parts of forage. Sheep can remain healthy with almost half as much. Horses, hogs, and rabbits require still less cobalt.

Animals, like plants, suffer from insect parasites. The Government has initiated scores of projects to combat such pests. None has had the spectacular success of what is known in Government circles as "Operation Screwworm."

The screwworm fly has red eyes, a blue body, and is about the size of a house fly. It gets its name from the fact that its larva is shaped like a screw. To cattlemen of Florida and other Southeastern states, it was a thing of horror. Females laid their eggs in open cuts or sores of cattle in such quantities that the infection could kill a steer in about 10 days. The little screwworm once was costing these cattlemen some 20 million dollars a year.

Agriculturists took up the problem. An airplane hangar at Sebring, Florida, was converted into a screwworm fly factory. Here billions of screwworms were bred, and in the pupa stage were submitted to Cobalt-60 radiation, not enough to kill them but enough to make them sterile.

During the mating season of the screwworm fly, the sterile flies were taken by plane, 50 million at a time, and released over Florida and the nearby states. The female screwworm fly mates only once and dies after she has laid her eggs. When the females mated with the sterile, factory-produced male flies, the eggs were infertile and would not hatch. As a result of this unique experiment, the screwworm fly population has disappeared almost completely from Southeastern states.

To keep food from spoiling is as important as raising it, particularly in our civilization where much of the population lives in cities

UNIVERSITY OF MICHIGAN

Irradiation enables produce to remain in storage without sprouting. The sprouting onions here did not have this preventive irradiation.

far away from the sources of food. Some of the most interesting work of gamma isotope radiation has been done in food preservation.

Gamma radiation in granaries kills insects and keeps grain from rotting. It prevents potatoes from sprouting when stored over a long period. Instead of softening, the potatoes remain firm and edible as at the time when they were harvested. Gamma radiation stops mold in oranges, tomatoes, and even slices of bread. It destroys the trichina parasites which make pork unsafe to eat unless it is thoroughly cooked.

Light gamma ray exposure has been found to increase the "refrigerator life" of a wide range of food, including hamburger, seafood, strawberries, and even prepared salads. Since gamma rays do not produce radioactivity, such foods can be eaten in perfect safety. Because there is no heat involved, there is no loss of vitamin content.

Under heavy gamma ray exposure, various vegetables, fruits, and meats stay fresh and edible for months and even years without any refrigeration. They have been tried on human volunteers with no ill effects. There are, however, disadvantages. Heavy radiation gives some food a peculiar taste or odor. Sometimes meat changes color and texture. The United States Quartermaster Food and Container Institute in Chicago has had a mammoth long-range experimental program to overcome these difficulties. If they succeed in making gamma-radiated food so it will look, and taste, and smell as good as nonradiated food, it will be the biggest event in food preservation since the invention of the tin can in 1804.

# Helping in the Hospital

## *Chapter* 9

A PATIENT lies on a specially built cot in a hospital room. Above him hovers a monstrous machine which looks like something Frankenstein might have built. It rotates slowly around him, its "face" always directed toward some special part of his body.

What is happening?

The man is suffering from cancer. The machine is a Cobalt-60 teletherapy unit. Within its "head" is a Co-60 source, a nugget of radioactive cobalt about the size of a walnut.

The Co-60 rays are helping the patient, not harming him. As the unit rotates around him, the rays are focused on the region of the cancer. They destroy the disorderly cancer cells more easily than normal cells. Because of the machine's rotation, the rays do minimum damage to surrounding tissue.

There are many such teletherapy units of one sort and another in hospitals throughout the world. Co-60 has a half-life of slightly over five years. It lasts a long time and is inexpensive to replace. Sometimes gamma-emitting isotopes with longer or shorter half-lives are used instead.

Co-60 is sometimes made in the form of small needles encased in platinum. The physician inserts the needle in the diseased tissue just long enough for it to kill cancer cells, removing it before it can hurt healthy tissue.

Gold-198 is also given by injection. It is made up in tiny pellets, or "seeds," hardly bigger than the eye of a needle and coated with platinum. These pellets are first made from stable gold; they turn radioactive under neutron bombardment in a reactor. With a miniature gun the physician shoots them into the cancer, 15 at a time.

They have the advantage that they need not be removed. Gold-198 has a half-life of 2.7 days. By the time its work is done, it has decayed to stable mercury. Modern scientists, instead of making gold from baser metals, as the medieval alchemists tried so hard to do, turn gold to mercury! But in the process they save many lives.

Tantalum-182 is a radioisotope of tantalum, atomic no. 73, a rare metallic element. For cancer injections the isotope is made up as a wire, sheathed in platinum, which can be bent in any desired form. Physicians use it to reach oddly-shaped cancer tumors, such as those that sometimes develop in the bladder.

In the next pages we shall mention a few specific types of cancer which radioisotopes are fighting. They are not the only soldiers against this most terrible of diseases. X-ray cancer treatment of course is very similar to that of the Cobalt-60 unit. Radium is still used for certain deep-seated cancer. Physicians advise drugs for some cancer patients. For others, surgery is necessary. No one method has yet been found to cure all cancers. Isotopes cure some cases and help others. For that alone they have earned man's gratitude.

Iodine-131 is the hero of the battle against thyroid ailments. The reason for this is that the thyroid gland attracts iodine more than any other element. Normally there is nearly 1,000 times as much iodine in the thyroid as elsewhere in the body.

The thyroid gland is located in the neck, just above the throat. It is shaped roughly like a butterfly, its "wings" joined by a bridge of tissue. A person with an inactive thyroid gland feels sluggish, finds it hard to collect his thoughts, may speak with difficulty. In extreme cases thyroid deficiency causes idiocy. When the thyroid gland is overactive all the body activities are speeded up. The patient is jumpy and nervous. He loses weight. His thyroid gland may swell until he develops a goiter.

To diagnose a thyroid condition, the physician gives the patient a glass of water in which a diluted solution of Iodine-131 is dissolved. Iodine-131 has a half-life of about 8 days and emits beta and gamma rays. An "atomic cocktail" this odd drink is called.

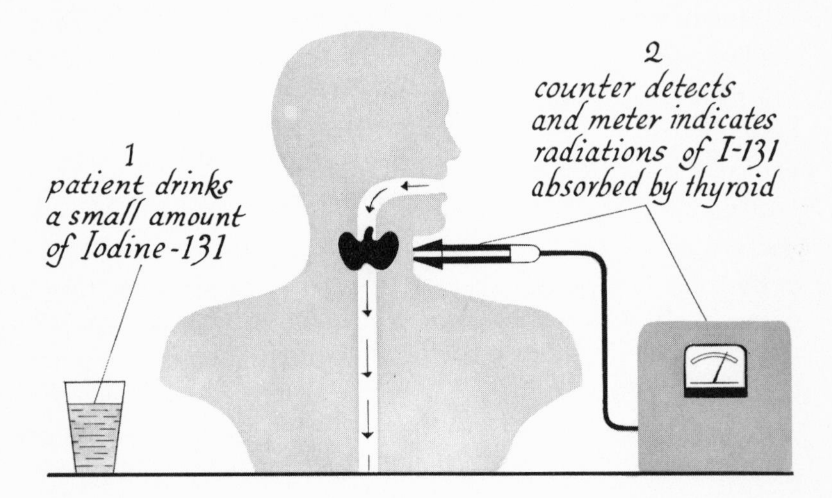


Ascertaining how much, or little, iodine the thyroid gland absorbs in individual cases.

Because of the special attraction the thyroid has for iodine, a good portion of this isotope with the stable iodine atoms heads for the thyroid gland. With a Geiger counter the physician or attendant can follow the travels of those atoms, and, depending on how fast the thyroid absorbs them, he can judge to what extent the thyroid is overactive or underactive.

Occasionally cancer develops in the thyroid. The thyroid cancer may spread to adjoining parts of the neck and even form "cancer colonies" in other parts of the body. Cancerous thyroid demands even more iodine than normal thyroid. I-131 rushes to the diseased areas, both in the gland and in the cancer colonies.

Instead of the familiar Geiger counter the physician more likely uses a detecting method known as the SCINTILLATION COUNTER. The scintillation counter gets its name because it records radiation as tiny flashes of light. It is better than a Geiger counter for detecting gamma rays. The scintillation counter is attached to another device which transposes the flashes of light to a sheet of paper, thus actually drawing a map of the diseased area.

I-131 diagnoses thyroid cancer with an advance patrol of tracer isotopes. Treatment is next in order. When other methods fail, the physician may call on a full "regiment" of I-131 to wipe out the disease. The isotope is given orally, like the "atomic cocktail." It heads directly for the cancer. Whatever damage it does to tissue is counteracted by the fact that it is saving the patient's life.

Temporarily, however, the patient becomes radioactive. For the first few days after his treatment, nurses will be changed every two days. His radioactivity diminishes with the eight-day half-life of the isotope. By the time he leaves the hospital, he will present no danger to his family and friends. This is an important point to remember, because of the unreasoning fear with which radioisotopes are sometimes regarded by people who know little about them.

Just as the thyroid attracts iodine, so bones and marrow of the body attract phosphorus. Phosphorus-32, the beta-emitting isotope we met in connection with its work on plants, both diagnoses and treats diseases connected with bones or bone marrow.

Red blood cells are formed in the bone marrow. Sometimes something goes wrong and they multiply too fast. This causes a dangerous ailment with the long name of *polycythaemia rubra vera*. If unchecked, the disease is fatal. To treat it, doctors inject the patient with a solution of P-32. This radioisotope heads for the bone marrow, where its beta rays succeed in slowing down the red blood-cell factory to a moderate rate. P-32 doesn't always cure *polycythaemia rubra vera,* but it keeps the disease under control, so that the patient lives longer and feels better than he would otherwise.

White blood cells also are made in the bone marrow. Their overproduction results in leukemia, a disease which in its acute form is almost invariably fatal. Sometimes it is caused by radiation exposure. Irène Joliot-Curie, who with her husband created the first man-made isotope, the short-lived Phosphorus-30, died of leukemia. Now P-32, brother to P-30, is successfully treating chronic forms of leukemia.

The most difficult and dangerous surgery is that on the brain. The best brain surgeon hesitates to remove a brain tumor unless the operation is absolutely necessary. Brain tumors attract iodine, somewhat as the thyroid does. I-131 is an invaluable assistant to the brain surgeon because it can help to map out the precise area of a brain tumor with the same techniques used on thyroid cancer. Thus the surgeon knows beforehand exactly where he will have to operate.

A spectacular advance in medical science is the treating of such brain tumors *without an operation,* a therapy which the Brookhaven Medical Research Center has been developing. This Medical Center has its own nuclear reactor purely for medical research. The treatment involves giving an injection of boron, atomic no. 5, into the tumor, after which the patient is wheeled into a small room built right into the reactor. He is completely covered except for a small portion of his skull. A small shutter in the wall next to the reactor is opened. Very briefly a tiny beam of neutrons bombards the tumor.

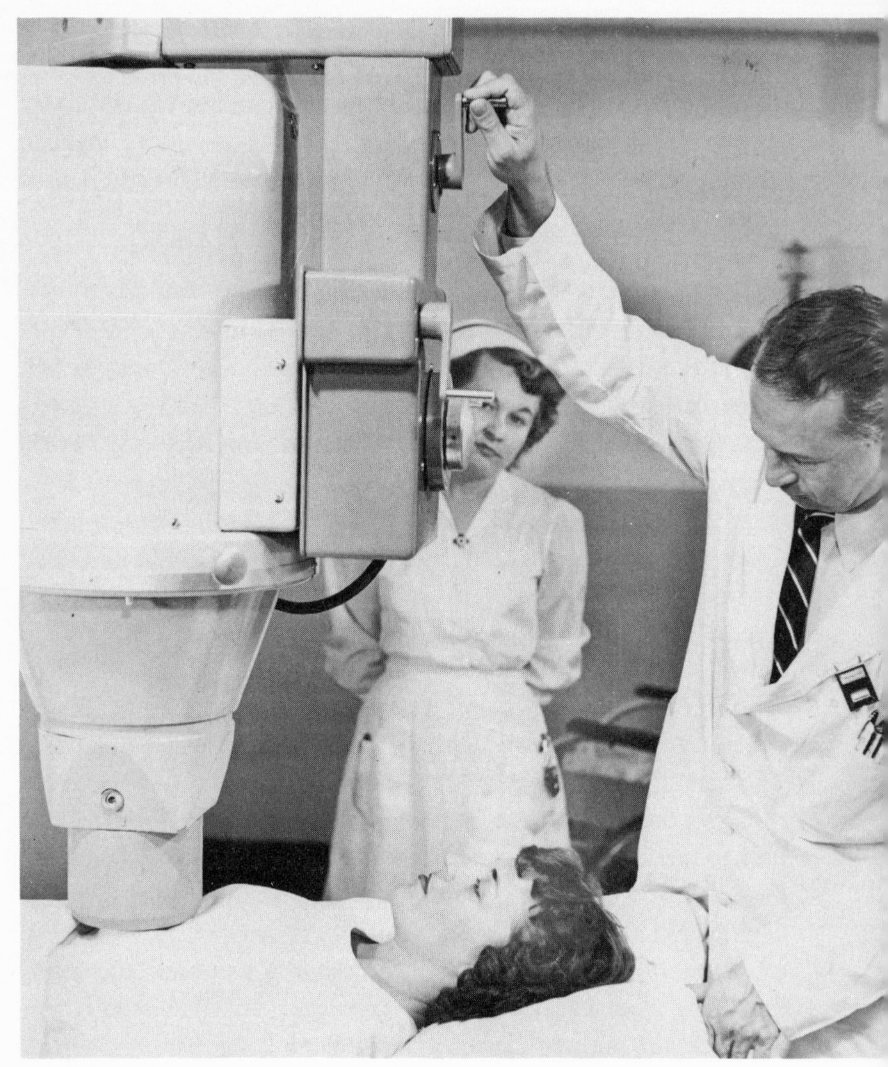

MEDICAL DIVISION, OAK RIDGE INSTITUTE OF NUCLEAR STUDIES

Demonstration of a teletherapy unit for treating cancer. The source of radiation is Cobalt-60.

Since boron is a "neutron swallower," the neutrons lodge in the nucleus of the boron atoms, changing them to a radioactive isotope which emits alpha particles in its brief half-life. The stream of neutrons is shut off, and the patient is wheeled out. His treatment is over. The newly-formed alpha particles have attacked and destroyed the brain tumor.

There are risks involved in this ingenious treatment and every precaution must be taken to protect the patient against overexposure. Medical scientists believe it offers fewer dangers than brain surgery and that many cases considered hopeless may be saved in this manner.

Although radiation always causes some damage to body tissue, it has one effect that is sometimes beneficial. Radiation makes it possible to perform transplants of foreign tissue. If mice are exposed to gamma radiation, it causes injury to the bone marrow tissue responsible for manufacturing blood. They can be kept alive by the transplanting of the bone marrow tissue of healthy mice. This transplant would not take if performed on nonradiated mice. Normally, mice reject such foreign tissue.

This same phenomenon applies to humans as well as to animals. It has proved possible to make kidney transplants from one person to another by first submitting the patient to radiation. The value of this technique had dramatic proof several years ago. In an atomic reactor accident, five Yugoslavian scientists had been exposed to intense radiation. They were flown to Paris for treatment, where French physicians gave them bone marrow transplants to replace the bone marrow destroyed by exposure. Although all five of the men were thought doomed, four of them responded to this treatment and eventually recovered.

Radioisotopes play a valuable but limited role as disease destroyers. As tracers, there is no end to the ways they can serve the men and women of medicine. As tracers, they are unique. The information they give is often unobtainable by other methods. Or if it is, tracers do the job more quickly and accurately. The thousands of tracer experiments done by biochemists and biophysicists are important to medical science, even though they have no immediate curative uses. But they may help to reveal physiological facts. The more the doctor knows about the healthy human body, the better equipped he is to understand what has gone wrong when someone falls sick.

In a laboratory experiment, scientists found that if a small amount of Iodine-131 is injected into the blood stream, it mixes evenly with all the blood in some 15 minutes. By measuring how much radioactivity is left in a single drop of blood, the scientist can calculate the total blood volume of a person's body. This technique saved lives in the Korean War. When wounded men were brought in from the field, doctors had a quick and easy way of finding out how much blood the men had left—and therefore about how much they had lost. The doctors therefore could prescribe the proper amount of blood plasma. The same method works for victims of automobile accidents or other catastrophes.

In research projects, the habits of iron atoms of the body have been extensively studied, as you saw in Chapter 7. The physician has been able to make practical use of these studies. Formerly, he prescribed large doses of iron extract to patients suffering from anemia, which is caused by a lack of iron. Iron tracers have shown that most of these large doses were wasted. The body will absorb only so much iron at a time. Now doctors prescribe a number of small doses of iron instead of one large one—and get better results.

Tracers provide information on insulin, the lack of which causes diabetes. They investigate the causes of hypertension. They collect data on certain ailments of the liver. They give the exact location of

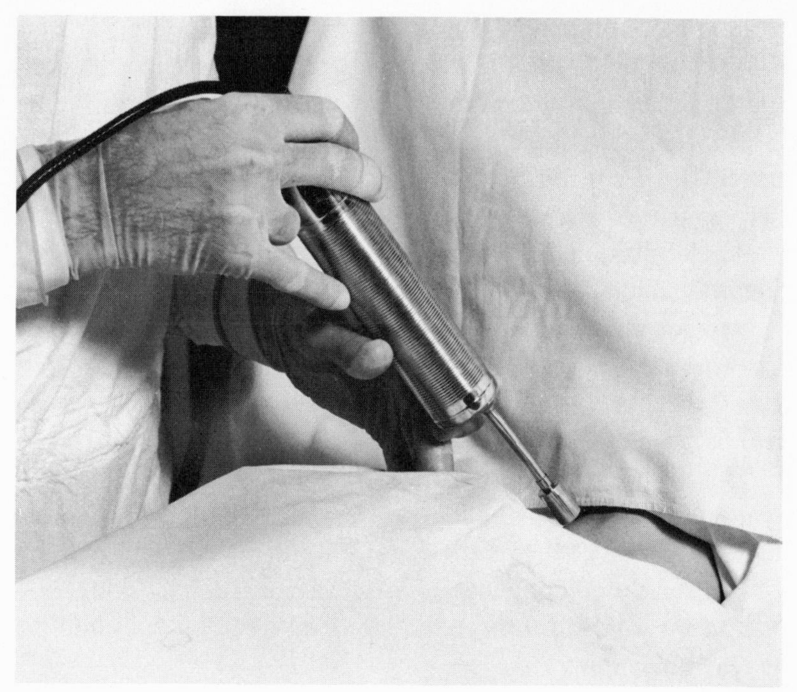

UNION CARBIDE CORPORATION

Using a miniaturized Geiger counter probe for diagnosis. To locate possible tumors, the probe follows a harmless amount of a radioisotope tracer as it travels through the body.

a blood block or constriction in the artery of a leg or arm. Tracers are even being used to study the extraordinarily complicated electrical and chemical processes involved in the brain's functioning.

They do a remarkable job, also, in explaining to doctors why certain drugs are effective in certain illnesses. For this they have to become part of these drugs.

Physicians sometimes prescribe a drug called digitalis as a heart stimulus. Digitalis comes from the leaves of the purple foxglove. It is very potent, one dose lasting many hours. The doctors did not know what happens to digitalis after it enters the human body. Scientists thought it was all gathered up by the heart, but there was no way to prove the theory.

This was the perfect problem for Carbon-14 to attack, since carbon is present in all living things. The difficulty was to find a way to make this radioactive carbon isotope a part of the drug. No chemist can make digitalis. Only the foxglove plant has that skill.

The solution was to have the radioactive carbon built into the foxglove as it grew.

This is the way it is now done. At the Argonne National Laboratories, outside of Chicago, is a curious sort of greenhouse. The carbon dioxide in the air of this greenhouse contains a strong proportion of Carbon-14 in its molecules. Plants, you will recall, breathe in carbon dioxide and release oxygen. Foxglove, grown in this atmosphere, makes its digitalis with an easily detectible amount of C-14.

From experiments with this radioactive digitalis, doctors have learned many new things about this drug, among them that most of it does not lodge in the heart, as was thought, but in the muscles.

In these strange, radioactive greenhouses, many other medically useful plants are grown. Cabbages, green peppers, tomatoes, for example. They give us ascorbic acid, or vitamin C. The poppy which supplies opium. From opium come the pain-relieving drugs, morphine and codeine. The deadly nightshade, or belladonna, plant. Its leaves and roots provide a drug with several medical uses, the best known being the dilation of the pupil of the eye.

One of the most interesting of the plants here is rauwolfia, which is of ancient origin, native to the Himalayas. Centuries ago the roots of rauwolfia were used to calm down mentally disturbed persons. Today it is made into the tranquilizing drug reserpine.

Science wishes to find out *why* these plant substances do what they do. *Why* does reserpine make people forget their anxieties and become calm and relaxed? Carbon-14 tracer experiments are unraveling such secrets.

Radioisotopes not only diagnose and treat illness. They help also sometimes to prevent it. As most people now know, the carriers of malaria and yellow fever are certain mosquitoes. The problem is how to keep an eye on them. By using radioisotopes such as Phosphorus-32 and Strontium-89 for tagging these pests, scientists are learning their flying habits and breeding places. Similar studies are being made with blowflies, sewer cockroaches, and other disease carriers. Scientists in Africa have launched a radioisotope project to fight the tsetse fly, which causes sleeping sickness.

These are only a few of the ways in which radioisotopes are contributing to medical progress. There are many others, too intricate for the scope of this book. But you can judge from the examples we have given how worthwhile it is to watch newspapers and magazines for the discoveries and inventions which nuclear scientists and engineers are making to protect and improve the health of the world.

## SOME RADIOISOTOPES THAT ARE HELPING DOCTORS

| | | |
|---|---|---|
| Arsenic-74 | Cobalt-60 | Radium-226 |
| Astatine-211 | Copper-64 | Radon-222 |
| Bismuth-206 | Europium-152 | Sodium-24 |
| Boron-10 and -11 | Gold-198 | Strontium-90 |
| Bromine-82 | Iodine-131 and -132 | Sulfur-35 |
| Carbon-14 | Iron-55 and -59 | Tantalum-182 |
| Cerium-144 | Lithium-6 and -7 | Thulium-170 |
| Cesium-137 | Nitrogen-15 | Xenon-133 |
| Chromium-51 | Phosphorus-32 | Yttrium-90 |

# Expediting Industry

## *Chapter* 10

INDUSTRY deals primarily with the making of *things*—things that are bought and sold, things that can be used to make other things.

In primitive society each man made his own bows and arrows, built his own house, wove his own cloth, and did his own hunting, fishing, trapping, farming, and preparing and carrying. Today nearly all the things for our daily living are mass-produced in factories for our constantly increasing population.

Here are some of the ways in which isotopes are helping industry to do its immense job.

### *Isotopes Judge Fullness and Amount of Things*

On the shelves of a supermarket are bottles, cans, packages of all descriptions. Pick up any of these containers and you can be pretty sure it will have the same content as any other of the same size and with the same label. Isotope gauges are at work in the packing machines so that no customer will get less or more in a container than is specified.

There are hundreds of different types of isotope gauges but the basic principle is similar in all. The gauge consists primarily of a radioactive source and a detecting instrument, such as a Geiger counter. Whatever thing is to be gauged, or measured, passes between source and detector. The latter records the rays from the source, and will show how dense is the obstruction between source and detector. In this way, the isotope gauge measures with the utmost precision.

Take a bottle of liquid soap. Likely, when this bottle went down its assembly line it passed between an isotope gauge and a Geiger counter. The gauge probably had a Cobalt-60 source, or some other gamma-emitting isotope. (Beta rays are too weak to penetrate glass.) Any bottle not properly filled would have caused too many or too few of the gamma rays to get through to the Geiger counter, and an automatic device would thereupon have switched that bottle off the assembly line.

Similar radioisotope techniques make certain that every can of noodle soup has the same measure of meat, broth, and noodles.

Isotope gauges control the air content in the manufacturing of foam rubber. They measure the water content of ore slurries in mines, and keep watch over the level of molten metals in foundries.

That cigarettes of the same brand are packed evenly with the same amount of tobacco is largely due to isotope gauges. They control the uniformity of material while it is flowing in a pipe, running along a conveyor belt or through a series of rollers, or dropping down a chute and even riding on a freight car!

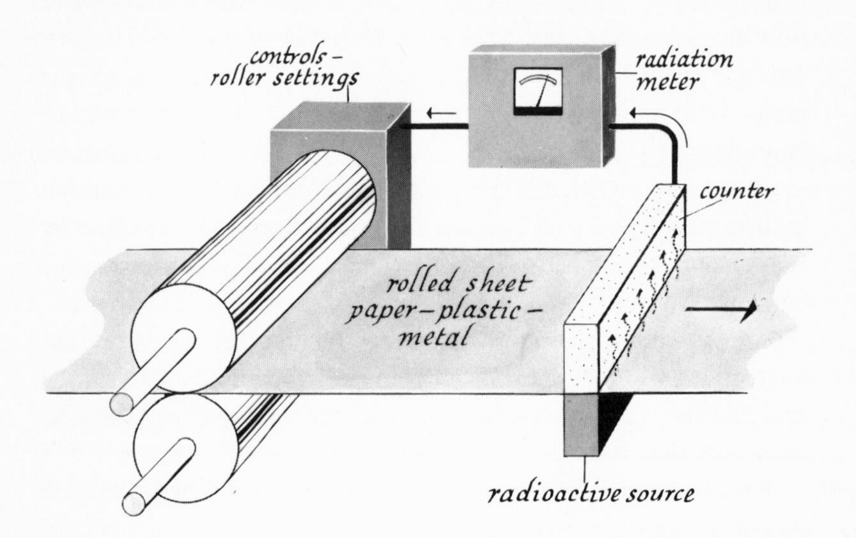

### *Isotopes Measure Thickness and Thinness*

Think of all the things that are in the form of flat sheets, or that are made from sheet materials. Paper comes first to mind. The paper on which the pages of this book were printed was once a long flat sheet. So were paper bags, cartons, heavy cardboards, valentines, and confetti. Rubber is manufactured in sheets and later made into everything from rubberbands to automobile tires. Aluminum, tin, copper, steel, plastics, roofing and floor coverings, coated fabrics, artificial leather, adhesive tape, sandpaper—these are just a few of the things that are produced in sheet form.

To maintain standards of good quality in their products, it is important for manufacturers that each type of sheet material should have a uniform thickness. In more and more factories, isotope gauges, checking the thickness and thinness of sheet material, like tiny watchmen, are replacing costlier and less accurate methods.

Gauges are used extensively in paper mills. As the sheet of paper is formed, and later finished, it runs through a long series of rollers. The gauge's radioactive source is usually stationed beneath the sheet. This source in most cases is Krypton-85, a beta-emitting isotope. Above the sheet is a special Geiger counter, which receives the beta rays that have pierced the sheet, and reports the number of them so that this shows on the scale of the indicator. The thinner the material, the more beta rays come through; the thicker it is the fewer the rays.

The operator can tell from the indicator whether the paper is running with a uniform thickness. If it is not, he can easily adjust the machine before very much off-standard paper has gone past him, even though the sheet runs through at speeds up to 1,000 feet a minute. In some cases the gauge is connected with a device which makes such adjustments automatically.

Isotope gauges are cheaper than other methods of doing the same work. No other method can detect such minute differences in thickness. One manufacturer of plastic sheeting claims he is saving $200,000 a year because of them. A tire manufacturer reports he used $250,000 less material because gauges prevented spoilage.

Since the operator has less cause to stand near the machines with isotopes doing his job, gauges help to avoid accidents. This is a major consideration when the sheet material is hard or hazardous to handle, as in the case of hot rubber.

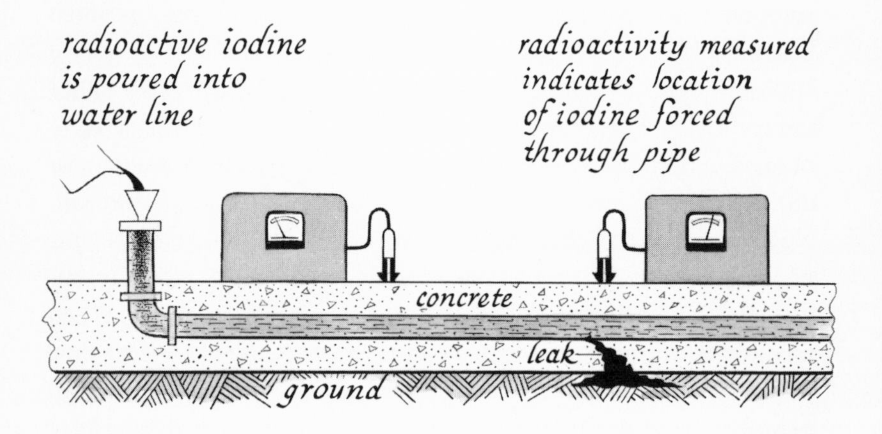


*Isotopes Find Leaks and Obstructions*

In a large housing development, a network of hot-water pipes was installed in the concrete floors for heating the house. Soon after the tenants moved in, the heating system stopped working properly. It was evident that there was a bad leak somewhere in the pipes. Isotope technicians were called in. They injected iodine tracers into the pipes, then flushed them clean, and then went from room to room with a Geiger counter. Very shortly they found the leak. Without the aid of the tracers the owners of the housing development would have had to pay thousands of dollars to tear up the concrete and replace it.

The underground cables of long-distance telephones are enveloped in lead. When holes occur in the lead, water seeps in, causing short circuits. Radiobromine tracers help to find those holes.

Radioisotopes have come into regular use for locating leaks in water mains.

An oil company which stores its fuel oil in slate quarries has developed a technique of utilizing tritium to check them for small leaks.

Tracer isotopes render a big service to the oil industry in another interesting manner. Oil companies often transport a wide variety of crude and refined oils by the same pipeline. Formerly it was most difficult to tell when the flow of one oil ended and another began. Nowadays the operator at the refinery simply injects Antimony-124, or some other radioisotope, between each type of oil. At the terminal point is another operator equipped with a Geiger counter. When the counter records the presence of the isotope, he knows the flow of one type of oil has ceased and it is time to prepare for the arrival of another. In this manner, tracers save the companies hundreds of barrels of oil a day.

### *Isotopes Test Things*

How does an automobile tire factory know whether its tires will stand up under road conditions? There used to be only one way of testing tires for durability: hire a man to drive on them. Several weeks might pass before the tires showed any noticeable wear.

Tracers do this task much more quickly and simply. When a tire is to be tested, factory technicians insert a small amount of Phosphorus-32 in the surface layer of the rubber before it hardens. The isotope reports signs of wear in less than five minutes—and down to a millionth of an inch.

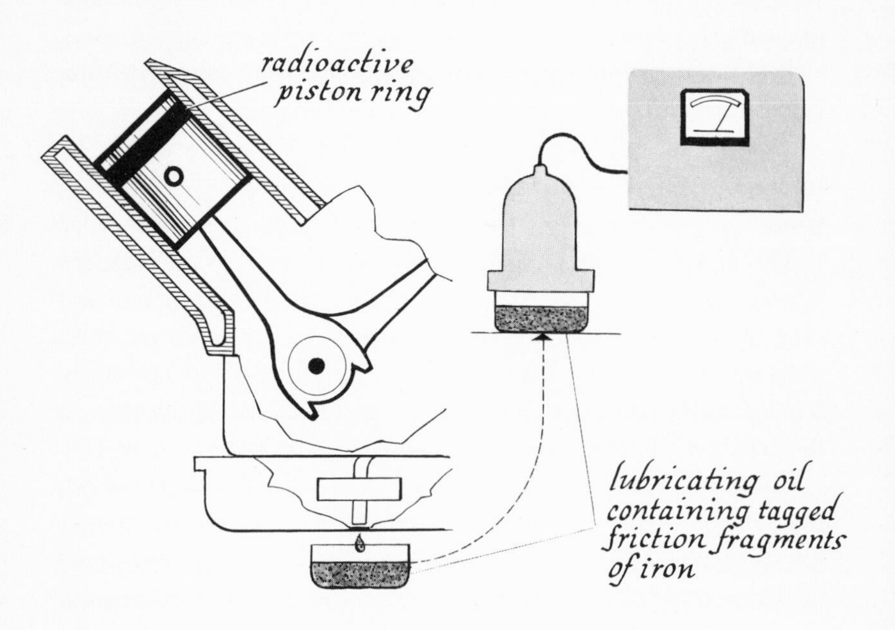


The radioisotope Iron-59 shows just how much any certain lubricant reduces the friction, and wear, within the unseen parts of a motor.

Suppose a factory wants to find out the wearing qualities of a piston ring. This is done by NEUTRON ACTIVATION. The factory sends the piston ring to a nuclear reactor where technicians submit it to neutron bombardment. The neutrons *activate* the iron atoms in the piston; that is, they change those stable iron atoms to radioactive Iron-59. On its return to the factory, the radioactive piston ring is put into operation for a few minutes. A tiny amount of it wears away under friction. By testing the lubricating oil around it for radioactivity, the technicians can judge the exact extent of the wear-down to the smallest fraction. Thus they can accurately judge how well the piston ring would stand up under weeks or months or years of service.

The wearing qualities of cutting tools and hundreds of other implements can be tested through neutron activation.

Tracers also report the wear and tear on the firebrick lining of blast furnaces where mineral ores are melted down. Ampoules of Cobalt-60, or some other gamma-emitting isotopes, are embedded in the lining at various depths, during the construction of the furnace. As the lining wears away from pressure of molten iron and slag, the ampoules melt and the isotopes send out their rays. With detecting instruments, the operator can tell just where and when damage occurs to the lining. The factory avoids the costly process of cooling off the furnace for periodic examination.

Calcium-45 tests the durability of paving asphalts. Some isotopes test the wear-resistance of floor wax. Some test the washing efficiency of detergents. Others have been put to work to study the hazards caused by detergents in our drainage system. Isotopes test many things in many ways.

### *Isotopes See Inside of Things*

All radioactive substances have the ability to take pictures of themselves when they are placed near a photographic film. In this, they are like x-rays. Radioactivity was first discovered by the French scientist, Henri Becquerel, back in 1897, because he accidentally left a piece of uranium ore on top of a photographic film.

When he developed the film, he found that the ore had taken a shadowy picture of itself.

When tracers take pictures of themselves in the leaves of plants or in living tissue, the process is called autoradiography, or self-photography. (See page 100.) But when radioactive substances, or x-rays, are used to take photographs of objects in the path of their rays, the process is known as RADIOGRAPHY.

By radiographs, Cobalt-60, and other isotopes with strong gamma rays, find flaws and cracks in the welds and the castings in ships and heavy machinery. It is as though the isotopes could see right inside the solid steel of which the weldings and castings are made.

The Cobalt-60 radiograph unit has a cobalt source about the size of a pea. The source is surrounded with heavy shielding, except that there is an opening for a stream of gamma rays from the cobalt source. The operator places the unit so that the rays are directed at the weld to be tested. They go straight through it, since gamma rays penetrate several inches of steel. On the opposite side of the weld is a photographic film. The developed film shows bubbles or other imperfections in the weld in a darker shade than the rest. In the same way, a medical x-ray reveals only the skeletal structure and not the flesh.

A big merchant ship has thousands of welds. If any one of them is imperfect, it could cause serious trouble. With a Cobalt-60 unit, a technician checks one after another of these welds in a few minutes.

X-ray equipment is also used for steel testing. The Cobalt-60 unit has several advantages. In spite of its heavy shielding, it is less cumbersome than x-ray equipment. Unlike x-ray, it doesn't require electricity. It can be moved around more easily. A special type of Cobalt-60 unit has been designed for parts of machinery that are inaccessible to x-ray equipment. This model has a long, flexible hose which can be inserted in a pipe or narrow opening. Compressed air drives a pellet of the cobalt isotope through the hose. The pellet makes its picture quickly and cleanly, and the air sucks it out again.

### *Isotopes Change Things*

Gamma rays, directed against certain substances, alter the structure of the molecules within those substances in a beneficial manner. This process is called CATALYST RADIATION.

Catalyst radiation may replace many of the chemical processes formerly employed for the same purposes. A good example of this is the vulcanization of rubber. Rubber is a soft, sticky plastic before it is vulcanized. Vulcanization makes rubber hard enough for tires or other things. Almost all the rubber we use has been vulcanized. Chemical vulcanization involves the addition of sulfur or sulfur compounds and takes several hours. Catalyst radiation on natural rubber vulcanizes it in a few minutes, without the addition of sulfur.

Catalyst radiation also plays a part in modern plastic manufacture. Plastics are man-made mixtures or compounds, formed of molecules that do not exist in nature. Thousands of things we use every day are made of plastics. Toothbrush handles, flower pots, toys, television cases—the list is endless. Through catalyst radiation better plastics are made.

For instance, the plastic called polythene used to melt before it reached the boiling point of water. Gamma rays now change the polythene molecules so that they resist heat. Now polythene can be used to make babies' bottles or other containers which must be sterilized in boiling water. Ovenproof plastic dishes are the result of catalyst radiation. There are any number of other uses for these new plastics created by catalyst radiation.

The oil industry is using catalyst radiation to develop new types of oil. As a result, one company has produced a motor oil which breaks up its own sludge, and consequently will not clog. The formula for this oil is so complicated that an electronic computer is needed to prepare it. Tracer isotopes keep track of the molecules as they are built into the formula.

Catalyst radiation is a new and exciting field. Technicians in many other industries are exploring its potential uses.

### *Isotopes Sterilize Things*

Drug companies sell a variety of sterilized products—bandages, absorbent cotton, toothbrushes, and surgical sutures, as well as antibiotic drugs, such as streptomycin and penicillin. The standard method of sterilization for such items has been the application of heat, which sometimes injures the product.

Gamma radiation sterilizes without heat. It is effective even after packaging, because gamma rays penetrate the container. Thus possible contamination between the time of the sterilization and the packaging can be prevented. There is no danger, since gamma radiation does not cause radioactivity.

### *Isotopes Produce Power*

In January 1959, the U. S. Atomic Energy Commission presented President Eisenhower with a radioisotopic generator—a miniature atomic power plant, about the size of a cantaloupe and weighing only about four pounds, complete with shielding. It was called SNAP III, the initials of "Systems for Nuclear Auxiliary Power." The source of its power was a thimble-size fuel-capsule of Polonium-210, which has a half-life of 138 days. Without refueling, it could generate electricity for some 90 days before its electrical output noticeably dropped off.

SNAP III was a milestone in isotope history. Since then there have been a number of other models of radioisotopic generators. Some have been put to useful work.

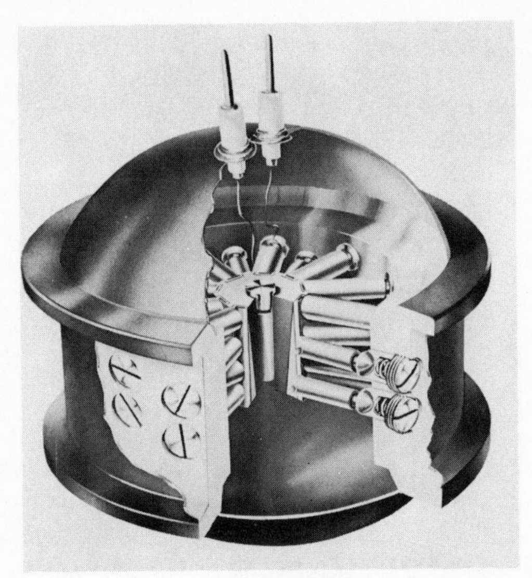

MARTIN MARIETTA CORPORATION

The famous SNAP III. The first generator using a radioisotope to produce a practical amount of power by making electricity directly from the energy of heat. It is 5½ inches high and 4¾ inches in diameter.

In the summer of 1961, the U. S. Weather Bureau and the Atomic Energy Commission set up the world's first weather station automatically operated by radioisotope power. This was on Axel Heiberg Island, which is but 750 miles from the North Pole and is a bleak, uninhabited place inaccessible during much of the year. It is one of many such points from which science needs frequent reports every day and night throughout the year in order to understand the ways of weather everywhere. The electricity for this unmanned station came from a generator using the heat made by the decay of Strontium-90. Although the main part of the station was

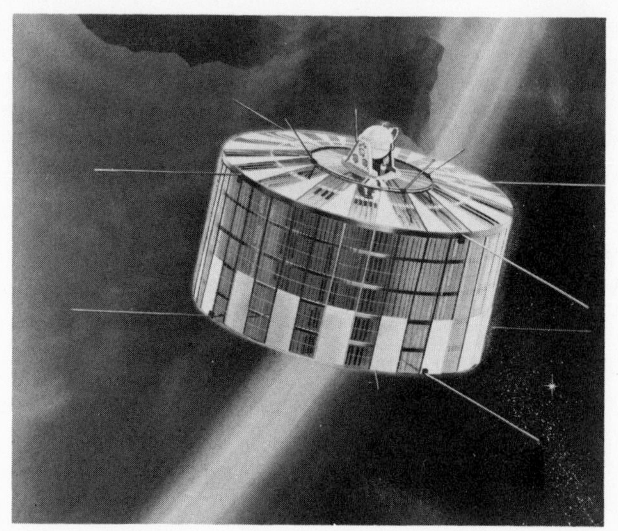

DRAWING BY HUMBERT OLIVARI, MARTIN MARIETTA CORPORATION

*Transit IV-A*, first nuclear-powered satellite in space. The Applied Physics Laboratory of Johns Hopkins University developed this signal-sending vehicle for the U. S. Navy.

The white ball on top, a SNAP thermoelectric generator, is only 5 inches in diameter, and will render service for over 5 years. The Plutonium-238 fuel is unbreakably sealed in for safety, and upon reentry into earth's atmosphere will burn up into particles too small to return in any significant measure.

eight feet tall, the generator itself was a cylinder only 20 inches high and 18 inches in diameter. See illustration, page 142.

Such generators are called THERMOELECTRIC because they

convert heat directly into electricity. (*Thermo* comes from the Greek word for "heat.") Thermoelectric generators require no moving parts, such as are in a turbine. Because they are small in bulk and give long service, space vehicles use them for the auxiliary power needed by the intricate instruments which gather space information and radio it back to earth.

The space satellite *Transit,* launched into orbit in the fall of 1961, was the first to carry a radioisotope-fueled auxiliary power plant. Its source was the transuranium isotope Plutonium-238, with a relatively long half-life of 89.6 years. It emitted a radio-frequency signal which all suitably equipped ships can receive. The signals enable the ship's navigator to calculate his position within a tenth of a mile.

On their satellite jobs, these small power plants can keep going for a year or more. They can be used on missions to the moon and serve as soft-lunar-landing generators.

## *Isotopes Give Light*

Phosphorescent substances glow in the dark when they are bombarded by subatomic particles. The luminous quality of radium dials on watches is not caused, as many think, by the radium but by the effect of alpha particles colliding with the phosphor, zinc sulfide.*

Phosphors bombarded by beta-emitting isotopes also produce a soft luminescent light. These isotopes are less expensive, less dangerous, and easier to handle than radium or other natural radioactive substances. Beta particles cause less deterioration of the phosphor than do the heavier alpha particles.

Tritium is the source for road signal lights, visible at night at a

* Some substances are called phosphors, or phosphorescent, even though they may not contain phosphorus.

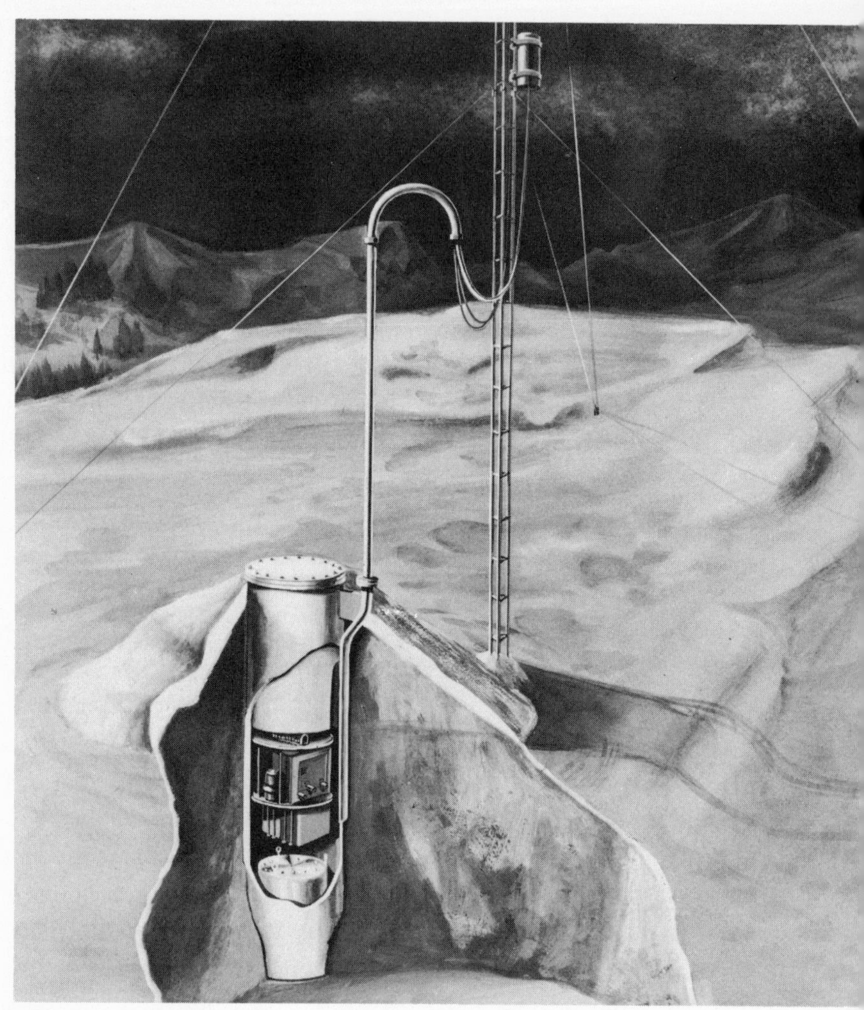

DRAWING BY HUMBERT OLIVARI, MARTIN MARIETTA CORPORATION

Cutaway sketch of the world's first weather station automatically operated by nuclear power. The generator is the cylinder in the lower part of the 8-foot container, over half of which is buried in the permanently frozen ground of this Arctic place.

distance of 100 to 200 feet. Isotopic light is not a substitute for electric light. It is never brilliant. It has at most twice the brightness of a sheet of white paper on a moonlight night.

The U. S. Navy has found uses for the softly glowing luminescent light which isotopes produce. In a submarine, isotope markers outline doors and hatches at night. In mines, safety markers illuminate tunnels and passageways. They illuminate switchboard dials and various measuring instruments. They have other potential applications for the consumer. They come in all colors, except red. Most important, they last for years without electric batteries.

Industrial uses of isotopes are multiplying so rapidly that you have to be on constant watch to keep up with them.

Because certain isotopes ionize air, they help to overcome static electricity, a serious industrial hazard. In textile and paper mills, for instance, the high-speed machines accumulate static which becomes a nuisance.

An illustration drawn with radioactive ink (using Nickel-63, which is a low beta-emitter) reproduces itself clearly on a photographic film.

Low-level gamma radiation from Potassium-40 will report the percentage of impurities in raw wool, at a considerable saving to the wool buyer.

Tracer isotopes are attacking the problem of "smog," or air pollution in large industrial cities.

The list goes on and on . . .

# The Clock Isotopes

## *Chapter* 11

HOW OLD is the earth? When did life first appear? How long ago did men learn to use fire, to make tools, to till the soil? How old is the oldest civilization?

Natural radioactive isotopes are helping archaeologists and geologists to find answers to these and many other questions about our unrecorded past.

Up until the turn of the century, the limit geologists placed on the age of the world was around a hundred million years. The discovery of uranium and its descendants gave them a new tool with which to revise their calculations.

Uranium deposits have existed since the earth was new. Down through the ages the isotopes of uranium have been disintegrating, each at the rate of its half-life. Uranium-235 has diminished by half every 713 million years. Uranium-238, with its half-life of 4.5 billion years, has decayed much more slowly.

Uranium atoms do not disappear when they decay; they change to isotopes of other elements. We have seen how that phenomenon takes place, both in natural and artificial radioactive isotopes. Since the earth began to take its present solid form, uranium ores and their descendants have remained mixed together, with exception of the gas radon, which is the first child of radium, and which at least in part escapes from its mineral home.

In every chunk of uranium ore which comes out of the mines, billions upon billions of unseen atom transformations are taking place every second. Within this uranium ore, U-238 atoms have 17 isotope descendants before they end in stable lead, some with half-lives of seconds or microseconds, some with half-lives of many years. In the same ore, U-235 atoms have 15 descendants before they too end in stable lead.

The radioactive change in elements goes on at a *fixed rate,* and that is why such a change can furnish science with a reliable measure of time.

As the facts about radioactivity became known, atomic scientists and geologists, working together, attacked an intricate mathematical problem. This was to use Uranium-235 and Uranium-238 as clocks to determine the age of the earth.

They knew the half-lives of these isotopes, and of their children and grandchildren and great grandchildren. They could compare the amounts of these radioactive families found in mineral ores. Such amounts are called "isotopic abundances." Isotopic abundances in radioactive elements are constantly changing, as atoms of one element change into atoms of another element. In stable Lead-206 and Lead-208, which are radiogenic, isotopic abundances are constantly increasing. See illustration, page 153.

After coordinating all this data, the physicists and geologists who worked on this project had a fair idea of how long ago the uranium ores were solid enough to hold together their families of descendants. But the scientists checked their conclusions with still further studies of radioactive substances outside the uranium families, such as Rubidium-87, with its incredible half-life of 50 billion years.

What conclusions did they reach? The estimate of 100 million years made by the earlier geologists turned out to be very modest indeed. Their radioactive witnesses gave evidence that the crust of the earth began to form some 2.8 *billion* years ago.* Nor was that all they revealed. Our planet has been in existence at least 4.5 bil-

* Through isotopic dating, some rocks found in Rhodesia are now known to be 3.4 billion years old.

lion years. The earth is at least 4.5 billion years old—a time span beyond human comprehension!

It takes radioactive substances with enormously long half-lives to help science clock the time that has passed since the earth's beginning. Such substances are useless for measuring the length of more recent eras. Even U-235, with its half-life of a mere 713 million years, measures in terms no smaller than about 20 million years. U-235 can no more indicate the less ancient spans of time than a grandfather clock can serve as a stop watch for measuring split seconds in a horse race.

An isotope suitable for shorter measurements is Carbon-14, which has a half-life of only 5,568 years. Measuring events of the past by Carbon-14 is called RADIOCARBON-DATING. Willard F. Libby, an American scientist, originated the idea of radiocarbon dating, in 1946, and later developed methods for perfecting this process. For his work in this field he was awarded the Nobel Prize for Chemistry, in 1959.

Carbon-14, which is made in quantity in a nuclear reactor, is rare in nature. There is only about one C-14 atom to every 800 billion atoms of its stable sister, C-12.

C-14 is being formed constantly by the bombardment of cosmic rays. Some travel almost at the speed of light and have such exceedingly high energies they can travel to the bottom of a deep lake or go straight through a yard of iron or lead.

When cosmic rays come through the earth's atmosphere, they collide with atoms of the atmosphere, causing the ejection of subatomic particles, which in turn hit other atoms. Primary cosmic rays are those which cause the first sets of collisions. Secondary cosmic rays are the streams of subatomic particles which resulted from those first collisions. About 78 percent of cosmic rays are believed to be made of protons.

C-14 is formed by cosmic rays in this fashion:

A proton from a cosmic ray strikes Nitrogen-14 which shatters into fragments and neutrons. One neutron hits another Nitrogen-14 atom, which swallows the neutron and ejects a proton, thus changing to Carbon-14, with six protons and eight neutrons.

The new C-14 atoms mingle in even quantities with stable C-12, and it goes everywhere that C-12 goes, just like any tracer isotope.

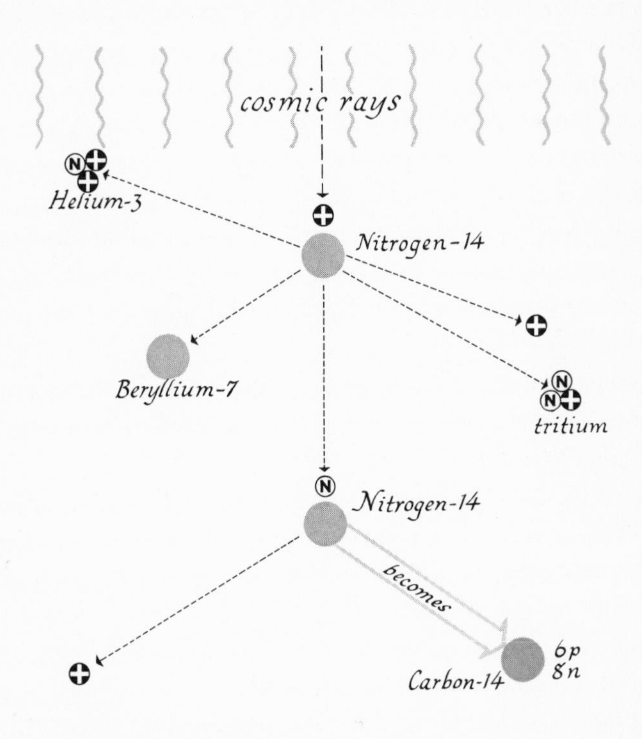


Every living thing absorbs carbon, both C-12 and a small proportion of the radioactive C-14.

A tree, as long as it lives, takes in carbon atoms, in the form of carbon dioxide in the air. It ejects each day about as many carbon atoms as it absorbs, so that the amount of carbon in the tree remains fairly unchanged. One in about 800 billion of these carbon atoms is C-14. The amount of C-14 in the tree might give off, say, 5,000 atomic breakdowns per second. Suppose you chop down that tree. As soon as it ceases to live, the carbon intake ceases. But the C-14 within it will continue to give off atomic disintegrations down through the centuries, in accordance with its 5,568-year half-life. In 5,568 years from now, the tree will only have half as much C-14, and will have only 2,500 atomic breakdowns per second.

In 11,136 years, with one quarter of the original C-14 left, there will be 1,750 breakdowns per second.

In 16,704 years, one eighth of the original C-14 will remain, giving off 875 breakdowns per second.

To measure how long ago a tree has been cut down, the scientist first measures its radioactivity, the atomic breakdowns from C-14. Then he compares the radioactivity with the amount that had probably been present in the tree when it was still standing. With the same technique, he can estimate the age of a plank of wood cut from that tree, a sheet of paper made from its wood pulp, and even its charcoal after a fire.

The older the object, the more faint the C-14 signals, and every precaution must be taken not to confuse them with other natural background radioactivity. Scientists have perfected such precise measuring instruments that now they can detect C-14 in bits of wood or wood products or other substances from trees and plants that grew on our earth 45,000 years ago.

The C-14 clock is of inestimable help to archaeologists and historians. Sometimes it confirms time estimates made in other ways. Sometimes it proves other estimates to be false. It helps to date many museum artifacts about which nothing was known.

In the tomb of an Egyptian Pharaoh was found a small sunboat,

A radioisotope "clock" made in the sky falls to earth. It enters into the tissue of vegetation, and then into the tissue of animals eating that vegetation. It stops entering when either of these stops living. It gets smaller and smaller at so definite a rate that it can show how much time has passed.

so-called because according to the Egyptian religion, the boat was intended to take the Pharaoh to the sun, Land of the Dead. Archaeologists, using other kinds of good evidence, estimated that the objects in the tomb had been placed there some 3,750 years ago. Scientists tested a plank of wood from the sunboat for C-14 and dated it as 3,620 years old, very close to, and thus confirming, the estimate of the archaeologists.

Another ancient boat was found in an excavation near Tokyo. By radiocarbon-dating, its age was established as 3,000 years. There were some lotus seeds in the boat. Even these were tested for C-14 content, and they proved to be about the same age as the boat. The odd thing about the seeds was that when they were planted they sprouted. They had been dormant for all of this long period.

Radiocarbon dating showed that a mammoth, found encased in ice in the Taimyr Peninsula in the Arctic part of Soviet Russia, lived some 12,000 years ago.

The same method dated the last Ice Age in North America. During that Ice Age, glaciers descended from the Arctic, destroying the trees in their way. The remains of one of these trees were tested with C-14 and it was found to have flourished 11,500 years ago. Geologists had believed that the last Ice Age was much earlier.

C-14 tests on charcoal outside the famous Lascaux Cave in France showed that the charcoal came from a fire built about 15,500 years ago. The primitive stone implements beside it had been used by Cro-Magnon men. Remains of another charcoal fire outside a cave in northern Iraq were given a similar test. The Stone Age family that warmed itself before the embers of the fire that had produced the charcoal lived about 30,000 years ago.

Some ancient scrolls were found near the Dead Sea. Their discovery caused great excitement among Biblical scholars although some doubted their authenticity. Radiocarbon dating proved they

BROOKHAVEN NATIONAL LABORATORY

Is the area where this ancient Mayan bowl was found its original home? Or had it been brought there from some other place? The archeologist here is scraping from it a minute sample which will undergo irradiation and a gamma-ray count. A fairly reliable answer to the question will result from a comparison with similarly treated samples of other objects that most likely originated in the same area of discovery.

were genuine. The linen wrappings of the scrolls were made from flax that had grown more than 1,900 years before, about the time of the birth of Christ.

The oldest known agricultural village in the world is Jarmo, in Western Asia. Once the people of Jarmo made flint sickles to reap grain, milled stones on which to crack the grain, built ovens in which to parch it. How long ago did these first farmers perform their daily chores? Scientists made a C-14 test on a fossil land-snail found in the village ruins, and they learned that it had been living 6,500 years ago. Other objects which were radiocarbon-dated, showed that agriculture had flourished in Jarmo some 9,000 years ago.

It was once thought that the Indians came to the New World only a few centuries ahead of Columbus. The carbon clock gave historians the evidence that men were hunting in Arizona around 10,000 B.C.

These are only a few out of thousands of radiocarbon tests which have helped archaeologists to form a clearer picture of the times of our early ancestors.

Another isotope clock is tritium, the third isotope of hydrogen. Tritium, like Carbon-14, is formed mainly by cosmic ray bombardment. It has a half-life of about 12½ years and is suitable for dating events which occurred up to approximately 75 years ago. Because it is so rare, its signals are extremely faint. Science has had to develop special techniques to catch them. One way is to concentrate it in water, of which it is a part, through evaporation.

In spite of the difficulties, some interesting work has been done in tritium-dating. Since cosmic rays produce tritium, it descends from the air into bodies of water in various parts of the world. The tritium clock has revealed that water remains in the air over the ocean about nine days.

By techniques similar to those used in radiocarbon-dating, tritium tells how long certain farm products, such as grain, have been left in storage. Through detection instruments, the scientists measure how much tritium is now present, and compare this to the

HOW AN ISOTOPE REVEALS THE AGE OF ROCK

(top) Long ago some molten material cooled, and held captive within it a certain quantity of radioactive substance, an isotope of uranium.

(middle) As time passed, the uranium's radioactive decay reduced this quantity at a certain steady rate, all the while turning the uranium into stable lead, which also increased at a steady rate.

(bottom) Today, by comparing the quantity of lead with that of the remaining uranium, science can tell just how much time has passed since this rock was formed. (See p. 144.)

amount of tritium that must have been in the product when it was first stored.

Meteorologists are developing tritium techniques to find out more about our water supply. Tritium can show how long water has been stored by nature in underground reservoirs. It can help in the study of naturally stored snow and ice. Glaciologists look to tritium for help in determining the age of glacier ice and snow in polar regions and on high mountains.

It is of considerable potential value to oceanographers, in studying water currents in the depths of the ocean. There is an immediate call for its services to locate places, at the bottom of the sea where water circulation is slow, to be used as safe dumping grounds for radioactive waste.

Tritium, as we have seen, does its clocking in terms of decades; radiocarbon dates events back to 50,000 years ago. Uranium isotopes clock geological events which took place hundreds of millions, or even billions of years before our time. Science is seeking ways and means to use other isotopes to fill in the wide gap between the radiocarbon and uranium clocks.

Two isotopes enlisted for this purpose are Potassium-40, which has a half-life of 1.3 billion years, and its daughter, Argon-40. Together, they have shown that a Tanganyika fossil-man, probably the first toolmaker, lived 1,750,000 years ago. Potassium-40 and Argon-40 are isobars, since their nuclei contain the same number of particles.

Beryllium-10, which has a half-life of 2.7 million years, about 1/300th that of U-235's 713 million years, is another isotope clock with great potentialities.

Atomic timing is still in its infancy. Already the clock isotopes have told us some remarkable things about the history of the earth and of the comparatively brief time man has inhabited it.

# Isotopes Tomorrow, and You

## *Chapter* 12

THE ISOTOPE industry was born in this country on August 2, 1946, when Oak Ridge Laboratories in Oak Ridge, Tennessee, shipped a few millicuries of Carbon-14 to a skin and cancer hospital in St. Louis. In the beginning it was treated like a stepchild, a mere by-product of the more spectacular uses of atomic energy. No longer a stepchild, this youth has grown to a giant.

It has a say in the manufacturing processes at automobile factories, oil installations, heavy machinery plants, and consumer-goods producers. In modern hospitals, isotope tracers for diagnosis and gamma radiation for treatment are routine procedure. Biochemistry and biophysics have taken great strides because radioisotopes have helped to unravel some of life's mysteries. Isotopes have made farming more efficient. They have given a helping hand to geology, archaeology, meteorology, oceanography, and many other sciences.

What will be the next feats of the isotopes?

Wrist watches which will run for years without rewinding? They have been made, experimentally, with a source of Promethium-147, the size of a dime.

Vacuum cleaners, run by isotopes? It is not impossible.

The tracing of underground rivers in arid regions? Work has been done in that direction. The most ardent isotope fans do not claim that isotopes *alone* will make deserts flower and become green, but their techniques will be valuable in any project to reclaim desert regions.

Isotopes will undoubtedly have more and more calls to help solve crimes. Nuclear scientists suggest several possibilities. If the owner of an explosives factory suspects dynamite is being stolen, he could have his technicians insert a small amount of gamma-emitting isotope in the dynamite slugs. A Geiger counter at the factory gate would detect the isotope and set off an alarm, should the thief try to pass.

All human hair contains a small amount of arsenic. When someone receives an overdose of this poison, the arsenic in the hair is increased ten times or so. Should the police suspect that arsenic is the cause of death, they could subject a few of the victim's hairs to neutron activation in a nuclear reactor. Neutron bombardment will turn the arsenic radioactive, making it easy to identify. (The same results could be achieved through a small neutron source without need of taking the hair to a neutron reactor.) Neutron activation analysis, as this technique is called, is particularly useful if the victim has been dead for so long a time that the remains afford no other clue. The cause of Napoleon's death, in 1821, was never quite ascertained until 140 years after, when the Department of Forensic Medicine at the University of Glasgow used this technique. They

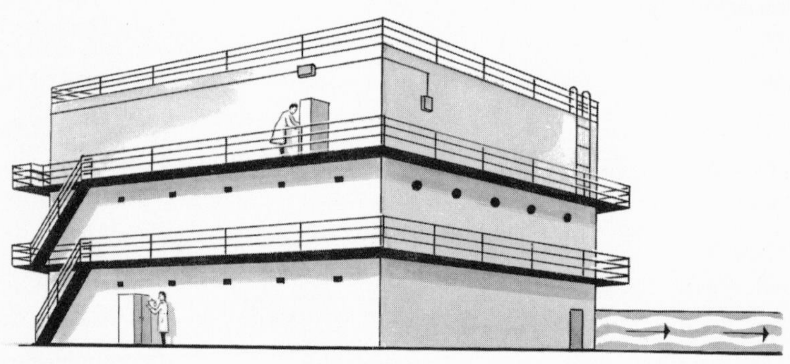

*REACTOR*
*provides heat for steam*

TURBINE
receives steam pressure
for rotating a spindle

GENERATOR
converts the energy of
mechanical motion into electricity

found that a hair of his contained over ten times as much arsenic as is normal!

One scientist proposes a rather elaborate way of detecting counterfeit bills. Every bank would have its own neutron source. All bills, as they are printed, would have a small amount of stable isotope stamped into the paper by a secret code. The bank would subject a doubtful bill to neutron activation in a neutron source. If the coded isotope doesn't appear in the Geiger counter detection, the bank officials can be sure the bill is counterfeit. There is nothing out of the question in this proposal, though it remains doubtful whether the benefits would justify the expense.

Thinking of possible uses of isotopes is a favorite game with nuclear scientists. It is a game anyone can play. Putting those ideas in practice is a much more complicated matter.

Scientists in many fields, from agronomy to zoology, have welcomed isotopes wholeheartedly. In industry there is still great room for expansion. In American industry, isotope techniques are not being utilized by many companies which might benefit by them.

One reason for this is lack of knowledge about their potentialities. The U. S. Atomic Energy Commission is the major source of information. The Commission had not at first been equipped to handle the vast publicity campaign needed to show businessmen how isotopes can help them.

Another difficulty is that each type of industry has different requirements, so far as isotope techniques are concerned. A radioisotope gauge suitable for measuring the thickness of paper will not serve for measuring hot rubber or some other product. Many industrialists hesitate to take a gamble on the cost of research and the building of new and untried installations.

Many people regard atomic energy for peaceful purposes with the same dread as they regard nuclear warfare and radioactive

MARTIN MARIETTA CORPORATION

The nuclear turboelectric plant installed at this Antarctic scientific station was delivered complete in one "package" by air. By using Uranium-235, this power plant does away with shipping huge quantities of fuel oil for running diesel engines and heating buildings in remote, small communities.

fallout. Sometimes this dread takes the proportions of hysteria.

Wherever there is radioactivity there is some danger. No one should approach radioactive substances without taking every precaution. No one should forget that the least carelessness can cause

BROOKHAVEN NATIONAL LABORATORY

To supply data for the science of genetics, this technician has just examined a bottleful of fruit flies through a microscope. Her task is to note and record any mutations (changes in offspring) that may have resulted from exposure to one or another form of radiation.

accidents. But unreasoning fear based on ignorance does no one any good. The more we know about radioactivity the more we shall be able to take advantage of the benefits it offers us and the better we can fight its hazards.

All industries, laboratories, and hospitals that use radioisotopes must have a license from the Atomic Energy Commission. To get a license, the applicant must show that his organization is equipped to observe high safety standards and that his staff has the training and experience necessary. For this latter purpose, the Government gives special courses in radioisotope research and industrial techniques. They are held at Oak Ridge Laboratories and other centers, last for several weeks, and are open to anyone with a college degree, preferably science majors. The courses are condensed and thorough, and give each student special instruction in isotope application for his own specialty. The students include doctors, nurses, laboratory technicians, mechanical engineers, oil experts, agriculturists, and persons of many other professions who feel their work will benefit with the addition of radioisotope techniques.

Perhaps some of you who read this book will want to specialize in radioisotope technology, not merely as an aid to some other line of work, but as a profession in itself. Radioisotope technology is roughly divided into three categories: production of isotopes, separation of isotopes, and use of isotopes. Since it is a branch of nuclear science, specialists in radioisotope technology need the same background as nuclear scientists.

What are the opportunities? How difficult is it? Does one have to be a special kind of person with a mind superior to the average?

The opportunities at this time are vast. There were some 15,000 qualified nuclear scientists in the United States in 1960. Some 40,000 were needed. There are always openings for those who are competent. Salaries are high, though few are likely to get rich.

The prime requisites for a nuclear scientist are a mathematical aptitude and an analytical mind. A nuclear scientist should also have a large fund of patience, perseverance, curiosity, and imagination. Lastly, he should not be the sort of person who believes everything he is told. The history of nuclear science is the history of men and women who had the courage to think for themselves.

Begin your preparation in high school by taking all the courses in mathematics and science that are offered. Some high schools now give laboratory work with isotopes in connection with science courses. Though big users of isotopes must have a license, one can purchase stable isotopes for home or classroom experiments without a license. You will find a list of suppliers on page 183. One of them, for instance, offers "more than 200 stable isotopes available from 50 elements."

One "isotope kit" contains ten microcuries each of the tracers Phosphorus-32 and Iodine-131. Another contains an assortment of nine isotopes in compound solutions. They sell from $7.50 to $18.00, though prices undergo revisions from time to time, usually downwards. The only restriction is that if the purchaser is under 21, he or she must give the signature of a parent or school faculty member.

The isotopes are shipped in dry state and amount to only a few trillionths of a gram. They are sufficient for the amateur to follow the travels of isotope tracers in plants and for other simple experiments, with the aid of an inexpensive Geiger counter or by making autoradiographs on an unexposed film. An excellent guide to their use is a pamphlet, *Laboratory Experiments with Radioisotopes for High School Science Demonstrations,* published by the U. S. Atomic Energy Commission. It can be purchased for 35 cents from the Superintendent of Documents, Washington 25, D. C.

Popular science books are excellent background material for the

ARGONNE NATIONAL LABORATORY

Chemist mounting part of a sample on a plate, in a study to judge the effectiveness of certain processes for separating transuranium elements.

future nuclear scientist. One important nuclear scientist claims that he first became interested in a scientific career because of science fiction. Biographies of the first atom explorers—Marie Curie, Lord Ernest Rutherford, Irène Joliot-Curie, and others—will portray both the trials and the moments of triumph of those who dared go further than anyone had gone before them.

In high school you can begin to think about college training, and select the college or university of your choice. In your first two college years you will go on to higher mathematics, differential and integral calculus, and advanced physics. In your junior and senior years, you will begin to specialize. Nuclear science and radioisotope technology require chemists, chemical engineers, physicists, metallurgists, biologists, and other specialists. It helps to know something about two or more of these groups.

Every radioisotope technologist should at least complete college. Some positions require a Master's or a Doctor of Philosophy degree. The further advanced you are in nuclear studies, the better equipped you will be to tackle difficult problems. You don't have to be a genius. Geniuses are as rare here as elsewhere.

There is hard work involved for anyone entering this field. There are rewards too. You will have security for yourself and your family. You will find yourself with congenial fellow workers, usually in pleasant surroundings. You will meet scientists from other countries and exchange ideas freely, for isotopes have no national boundaries. Their benefits are for all alike.

The mighty army of isotopes offers its services to all of us. It is one proof that the atom was not split in vain. Its future depends on the skills of the young generation of scientists. One can be sure it will continue to grow and to do more things for more people and do them better and better.

# APPENDIX

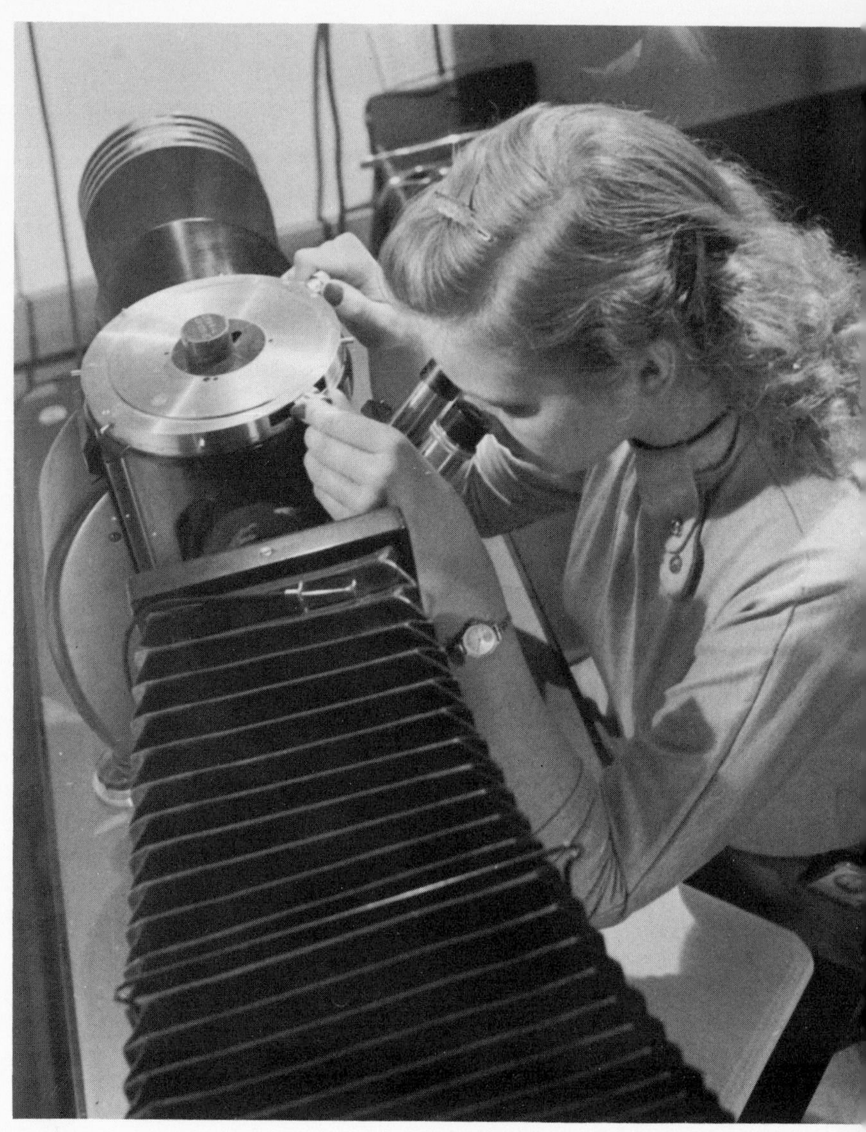

ARGONNE NATIONAL LABORATORY

Research technician examining through a microscope a specimen of uranium for its microstructure. This is preparatory to the making of a photomicrograph. Note the camera bellows in foreground.

LIST OF ELEMENTS (Arranged alphabetically by symbol.)

| SYMBOL | NAME | ATOMIC NUMBER | DATE OF DISCOVERY |
|---|---|---|---|
| A | Argon | 18 | 1894 |
| Ac | Actinium | 89 | 1899 |
| Ag | Silver (*argentum**) | 47 | ancient |
| Al | Aluminum | 13 | 1827 |
| Am | Americium | 95 | 1944 |
| As | Arsenic | 33 | medieval |
| At | Astatine | 85 | 1940 |
| Au | Gold (*aurum**) | 79 | ancient |
| B | Boron | 5 | 1808 |
| Ba | Barium | 56 | 1808 |
| Be | Beryllium | 4 | 1797 |
| Bi | Bismuth | 83 | medieval |
| Bk | Berkelium | 97 | 1949 |
| Br | Bromine | 35 | 1825 |
| C | Carbon | 6 | ancient |
| Ca | Calcium | 20 | 1808 |
| Cd | Cadmium | 48 | 1817 |
| Ce | Cerium | 58 | 1803 |
| Cf | Californium | 98 | 1950 |
| Cl | Chlorine | 17 | 1774 |
| Cm | Curium | 96 | 1944 |
| Co | Cobalt | 27 | 1737 |
| Cr | Chromium | 24 | 1797 |
| Cs | Cesium | 55 | 1860 |
| Cu | Copper (*cuprum**) | 29 | ancient |
| Dy | Dysprosium | 66 | 1886 |
| E | Einsteinium | 99 | 1952 |
| Er | Erbium | 68 | 1843 |
| Eu | Europium | 63 | 1901 |
| F | Fluorine | 9 | 1886 |
| Fm | Fermium | 100 | 1953 |

| | | | |
|---|---|---|---|
| Fr | Francium | 87 | 1939 |
| Fe | Iron (*ferrum**) | 26 | ancient |
| Ga | Gallium | 31 | 1875 |
| Gd | Gadolinium | 64 | 1886 |
| Ge | Germanium | 32 | 1886 |
| H | Hydrogen | 1 | 1766 |
| He | Helium | 2 | 1868 |
| Hf | Hafnium | 72 | 1923 |
| Hg | Mercury (*hydragyrum**) | 80 | ancient |
| Ho | Holmium | 67 | 1879 |
| I | Iodine | 53 | 1811 |
| In | Indium | 49 | 1863 |
| Ir | Iridium | 77 | 1804 |
| K | Potassium (*kalium**) | 19 | 1807 |
| Kr | Krypton | 36 | 1898 |
| La | Lanthanum | 57 | 1839 |
| Li | Lithium | 3 | 1817 |
| Lu | Lutetium | 71 | 1907 |
| Lw | Lawrencium | 103 | 1961 |
| Mg | Magnesium | 12 | 1808 |
| Mn | Manganese | 25 | 1774 |
| Mo | Molybdenum | 42 | 1781 |
| Mv | Mendelevium | 101 | 1955 |
| N | Nitrogen | 7 | 1772 |
| Na | Sodium (*natrium**) | 11 | 1807 |
| Nb | Niobium | 41 | 1801 |
| Nd | Neodymium | 60 | 1885 |
| Ne | Neon | 10 | 1898 |
| Ni | Nickel | 28 | 1751 |
| No | Nobelium | 102 | 1957 |
| Np | Neptunium | 93 | 1940 |
| O | Oxygen | 8 | 1771 |
| Os | Osmium | 76 | 1804 |
| P | Phosphorus | 15 | 1669 |
| Pa | Protactinium | 91 | 1917 |
| Pb | Lead (*plumbum**) | 82 | ancient |

| | | | |
|---|---|---|---|
| Pd | Palladium | 46 | 1803 |
| Pm | Promethium | 61 | 1945 |
| Po | Polonium | 84 | 1898 |
| Pr | Praseodymium | 59 | 1885 |
| Pt | Platinum | 78 | 16th century |
| Pu | Plutonium | 94 | 1940 |
| Ra | Radium | 88 | 1898 |
| Rb | Rubidium | 37 | 1861 |
| Re | Rhenium | 75 | 1925 |
| Rh | Rhodium | 45 | 1803 |
| Rn | Radon | 86 | 1900 |
| Ru | Ruthenium | 44 | 1844 |
| S | Sulfur | 16 | ancient |
| Sb | Antimony | 51 | medieval |
| Sc | Scandium | 21 | 1879 |
| Se | Selenium | 34 | 1818 |
| Si | Silicon | 14 | 1824 |
| Sm | Samarium | 62 | 1879 |
| Sn | Tin (*stannum**) | 22 | ancient |
| Sr | Strontium | 38 | 1808 |
| Ta | Tantulum | 73 | 1802 |
| Tb | Terbium | 65 | 1843 |
| Tc | Technetium | 43 | 1937 |
| Te | Tellurium | 52 | 1783 |
| Th | Thorium | 90 | 1828 |
| Ti | Titanium | 22 | 1791 |
| Tl | Thallium | 81 | 1861 |
| Tm | Thulium | 69 | 1879 |
| U | Uranium | 92 | 1789 |
| V | Vanadium | 23 | 1830 |
| W | Tungsten (*wolfram**) | 74 | 1783 |
| Xe | Xenon | 54 | 1898 |
| Y | Yttrium | 39 | 1794 |
| Yb | Ytterbium | 70 | 1878 |
| Zn | Zinc | 30 | 17th century |
| Zr | Zirconium | 40 | 1789 |

* Former name

# THE PERIODIC TABLE

| | | | | | | | | |
|---|---|---|---|---|---|---|---|---|
| 1 H | | | | | | | | |
| 3 Li | 4 Be | | | | | | | |
| 11 Na | 12 Mg | | | | | | | |
| 19 K | 20 Ca | 21 Sc | 22 Ti | 23 V | 24 Cr | 25 Mn | 26 Fe | 27 Co |
| 37 Rb | 38 Sr | 39 Y | 40 Zr | 41 Nb | 42 Mo | 43 Tc | 44 Ru | 45 Rh |
| 55 Cs | 56 Ba | | 72 Hf | 73 Ta | 74 W | 75 Re | 76 Os | 77 Ir |
| 87 Fr | 88 Ra | | | | | | | |

THE LANTHANIDE

| 57 La | 58 Ce | 59 Pr | 60 Nd | 61 Pm | 62 Sm |
|---|---|---|---|---|---|

THE ACTINIDE

| 89 Ac | 90 Th | 91 Pa | 92 U | 93 Np | 94 Pu |
|---|---|---|---|---|---|

# OF THE ELEMENTS

| | | | | | | | | NOBLE (INERT) GASES |
|---|---|---|---|---|---|---|---|---|
| | | | | | | | | 2<br>He |
| | | | 5<br>B | 6<br>C | 7<br>N | 8<br>O | 9<br>F | 10<br>Ne |
| | | | 13<br>Al | 14<br>Si | 15<br>P | 16<br>S | 17<br>Cl | 18<br>Ar |
| 28<br>Ni | 29<br>Cu | 30<br>Zn | 31<br>Ga | 32<br>Ge | 33<br>As | 34<br>Se | 35<br>Br | 36<br>Kr |
| 46<br>Pd | 47<br>Ag | 48<br>Cd | 49<br>In | 50<br>Sn | 51<br>Sb | 52<br>Te | 53<br>I | 54<br>Xe |
| 78<br>Pt | 79<br>Au | 80<br>Hg | 81<br>Ti | 82<br>Pb | 83<br>Bi | 84<br>Po | 85<br>At | 86<br>Rn |

ELEMENTS

| 63 | 64 | 65 | 66 | 67 | 68 | 69 | 70 | 71 |
|---|---|---|---|---|---|---|---|---|
| Eu | Gd | Tb | Dy | Ho | Er | Tm | Yb | Lu |

ELEMENTS

| 95 | 96 | 97 | 98 | 99 | 100 | 101 | 102 | 103 |
|---|---|---|---|---|---|---|---|---|
| Am | Cm | Bk | Cf | E | Fm | Mv | No | Lw |

## SOME IMPORTANT DATES IN THE ISOTOPE STORY

1895 William Roentgen discovers x-rays.

1896 Henri Becquerel discovers radioactivity.

1897 J. J. Thomson identifies the electron as the basic particle in electricity and as present in all atoms.

1898-9 Marie Curie discovers the radioactive elements radium and polonium.

1903 Ernest Rutherford and Frederick Soddy discover the natural transmutation of radioactive elements.

1905 Albert Einstein's famous equation $E = mc^2$ is given to the world.

1911 C. T. R. Wilson perfects his cloud chamber, by means of which the trails of subatomic particles can be photographed.
Rutherford proves that the atom is mostly empty space, with a small electrically charged nucleus.

1913 Soddy names isotopes, discovered almost simultaneously by him and two other scientists.
Niels Bohr explains the orbits of electrons around the nucleus.
John Joly and Rutherford suggest the first use of radioactive decay as a means for ascertaining age of substances—in this case, rocks.

1913-14 Henry Moseley's "Law of Atomic Numbers" is announced.

1919 Rutherford performs the first man-made transmutation of the elements.
F. W. Aston invents the mass spectrograph by which isotopes of neon and other nonmetallic elements can be separated.

1920 The proton is named.

1923 The first biological tracer experiment is made. George von Hevesy uses natural radioactive lead to investigate the uptake of lead in plants.

1928 Hans Geiger and W. Mueller invent the Geiger-Mueller counter (popularly known as the Geiger counter), developed from earlier models.

1931 The first atomic transmutation in a particle accelerator (lithium into helium) is made in England by John Cockroft and E. T. S. Walton. It is repeated in America by Ernest Lawrence in his cyclotron.

1931 H. C. Urey discovers and separates heavy hydrogen.

1932 Frédéric and Irène Joliot-Curie discover artificial radioactive isotopes.
C. D. Anderson discovers the positron.

1934 Tritium is made artificially by Rutherford, Oliphant, and Harteck.

1938-9 The atom is fissioned.

1942 The first nuclear reactor is built in Chicago.

1945 Nuclear bombs are exploded over Hiroshima and Nagasaki.

1946 The isotope industry is born at Oak Ridge, Tennessee.

1955 *Nautilus,* the first submarine propelled by nuclear power, goes into service.

1957 Radiocarbon dating is originated and developed by Willard Libby.

1959 SNAP III, the first working model of an "isotope power plant," is made.

1961 The first radioisotope-powered weather station is established, in the Arctic.
The space satellite *Transit* is first to carry a radioisotope-fueled auxiliary power plant.

1962 *Savannah,* the first merchant ship propelled by nuclear power, makes its first voyage.

## THE TRANSURANIUM ELEMENTS

| ATOMIC NO. & SYMBOL | NAME | DATE OF DISCOVERY | NAMED IN HONOR OF |
|---|---|---|---|
| 93 Np | Neptunium | 1940 | Neptune, first planet beyond Uranus |
| 94 Pu | Plutonium | 1940 | Pluto, second planet beyond Uranus |
| 95 Am | Americium | 1944 | The Americas |
| 96 Cm | Curium | 1944 | Marie and Pierre Curie |
| 97 Bk | Berkelium | 1949 | Berkeley, Calif., home of Univ. of California where much transuranic research was done |
| 98 Cf | Californium | 1950 | The state and its University |
| 99 E | Einsteinium | 1952 | Albert Einstein |
| 100 Fm | Fermium | 1953 | Enrico Fermi |
| 101 Mv | Mendelevium | 1955 | Dmitri Mendeleev |
| 102 No | Nobelium | 1957 | Alfred Nobel |
| 103 Lw | Lawrencium | 1961 | Ernest O. Lawrence |

## GLOSSARY OF NUCLEAR TERMS

ALPHA RAYS. One of the three rays from radioactive substances. An alpha ray is made up of a stream of alpha particles. Each alpha particle is composed of two neutrons and two protons. It is identical with the nucleus of a helium atom. *See also* BETA RAYS, GAMMA RAYS.

ATOM. The smallest particle into which an element can be divided and retain its identity as an element.

ATOMIC NUMBER. The atomic number of an element corresponds to the number of protons or electrons in its atoms.

ATOMIC WEIGHT. The relative weights of atoms of different elements, or of subatomic particles. All atomic weights are calculated on the basis of a fixed weight of 12 for carbon.

AUTORADIOGRAPHY. Self-photographs of radioactive substances made by placing the radioactive material next to photographic film.

BACKGROUND RADIOACTIVITY. Radiation from natural radioactive substances and cosmic rays.

BETA RAYS. One of the three rays from radioactive substances. Beta rays are made up of streams of beta particles. A beta particle is an electron.

BOMBARDMENT. A stream of subatomic particles directed like bullets against a substance. In a nuclear reactor radioactive isotopes are made from stable substances by neutron bombardment.

BREEDER. *See* NUCLEAR REACTOR.

BULK SHIELDING REACTOR. *See* NUCLEAR REACTOR—SWIMMING POOL. . . .

CATALYST RADIATION. Gamma radiation used to cause molecular changes within a substance.

CHEMICAL (——PROPERTY, ——CHANGE, ETC.). The ability or inability of elements to combine with each other in the form of compounds, or of elements to associate without affecting the stability of their atoms. Chemical changes do not involve particles and arrangements within atomic nuclei. *See* NUCLEAR (BOMB, ENERGY, etc.).

CLOUD CHAMBER. An apparatus for detecting and measuring radiations by making the tracks of particles visible as fine lines of cloud.

COFFIN. Atomic slang for the reactor's lead containers in which the stringers are kept.

COMPOUND. A substance made up of identical molecules, each of which is made up of various atoms. E.g., water, salt.

CONTROL RODS. Part of a nuclear reactor. Control rods, made of a neutron-absorbing substance such as boron or cadmium, are inserted into the reactor to slow down or stop the fissioning of atoms, or pulled out to increase the rate of fissioning.

COOLANT. Air, gas, or liquid which circulates through a nuclear reactor to lower the high temperatures.

COSMIC RAYS. Radiation, of enormous penetrating power, which comes from outer space.

CURIE. The rate at which radioactive isotopes decay. One curie is equivalent to the radiation from one gram of radium, or 37 billion atomic disintegrations per second. Named after Marie Curie, discoverer of radium. A MILLECURIE is a thousandth of a curie. A MICROCURIE is a millionth of a curie.

DEUTERIUM. An isotope of hydrogen, containing one neutron and one proton in the atomic nucleus. Also called Hydrogen-2 or heavy hydrogen.

DEUTERONS. The nucleus of heavy hydrogen or deuterium atoms, with one neutron and one proton.

ELECTRON. A negatively charged particle which revolves around the atomic nucleus.

ELEMENT. A basic substance of matter which cannot be changed chemically but is changed in the process of radioactivity.

FISSION. The splitting of the atomic nucleus of heavy elements roughly into two parts, which are themselves atomic nuclei. The fissioning releases vast amounts of energy, and some free neutrons.

FISSION FRAGMENTS. The new atomic nuclei which are formed in the process of fissioning, usually radioactive.

FUEL. The uranium or plutonium in a nuclear reactor, atoms of which are fissioned in a chain reaction when the reactor is in operation.

FUSION. The joining together of atomic nuclei of light elements to form atomic nuclei of heavier elements.

GAMMA RAYS. One of the three rays from radioactive substances. Like x-rays, they are in the form of energy, not matter.

GEIGER COUNTER. A device for measuring radioactivity by recording radiation as electrical impulses.

HALF-LIFE. The length of time it takes half of the atoms of a radioactive substance to decay.

HEAVY HYDROGEN. The same as deuterium or Hydrogen-2.

HEAVY WATER. Water with heavy hydrogen in its molecules.

HOT CELL. A room where highly radioactive substances are processed and where extreme safety precautions must be observed.

ION. An electrically charged atom. A neutral atom which has lost an electron becomes positively charged; one which has gained an electron becomes negatively charged. One negative ion and one positive ion, each with the same amount of charge, make an ION PAIR.

IONIZING RADIATION. Any radiation which gives atoms an electric charge, that is, turns them into ions, as it passes among them.

IRRADIATION HOLE. Opening in a reactor where substances to be made radioactive are inserted.

ISOBARS. Isotopes which have the same mass numbers and the same atomic weight but which belong to different elements. Examples: Thorium-234 and Protoactinium-234; Potassium-40, Calcium-40, and Argon-40.

ISOTOPES. The atoms which have the same chemical properties and the same place in the Periodic Table as the other atoms of their element but which have a different atomic weight because of having within their nuclei a larger or smaller number of neutrons. The atoms of an isotope may be stable or unstable. An isotope composed of stable atoms may be either naturally or artificially radioactive. The term RADIOISOTOPES refers usually to the man-made radioactive isotopes.

MASS. The amount of matter in a body; that is, how many particles it contains. *Weight* differs from *mass* in that the weight of a thing is a measure of how much force it shows in response to gravity, while its mass is a measure regarded apart from gravity.

MASS NUMBER. The sum of the neutrons and protons in the atomic nucleus. This number usually approximates the atomic weight of an element.

MASS SPECTROGRAPH and SPECTROMETER. Instruments for measuring atomic masses. They are useful in studying atomic structure, and since they separate atoms according to weight, they indicate the different isotopes within an element.

MICRONUTRIENTS. Minute amounts of metallic elements necessary to the health of plant and animal life.

MIXTURE. A combination of two or more compounds, or a combination of compounds and pure elements.

MODERATOR. Part of a nuclear reactor. A substance such as heavy water or graphite which slows down neutrons so they fission target-atoms more effectively. Not to be confused with control rods.

MOLECULE. The smallest part of a compound which retains the identity of that compound. A molecule may be made up of atoms of the same element or atoms of different elements.

MUTATION. A change in a basic characteristic of any form of plant or animal life. Mutations occur rarely in nature. They can be produced frequently through gamma radiation. Only a small proportion of mutations are beneficial.

NEUTRON. One of the three major subatomic particles in the atom, the other two being the proton and the electron. Neutrons and protons are within the atomic nucleus; electrons revolve around the nucleus. Unlike the first two particles, neutrons have no electric charge. FREE NEUTRONS are neutrons liberated by nuclear fission. SLOW NEUTRONS are low-energy neutrons. They hit targets more readily than do neutrons traveling at higher energies.

NEUTRON ACTIVATION. The submitting of any substance to neutron bombardment, from a neutron source, or in a nuclear reactor. The neutrons *activate,* i.e., produce, radioactive isotopes within that substance.

NEUTRON CHAIN REACTION. Neutrons that are released by a fissioned atom, and that then fission other atoms, which release more neutrons, which repeat the process ever increasingly.

NEUTRON SOURCE. A solution that ejects neutrons, such as a mixture of radium and beryllium.

NUCLEAR (——ENERGY, ——BOMB). A more accurate term than the popular "atomic" when used with the words "energy" or "bomb," since the energy liberated when an atom fissions comes from the nucleus. The studies of *sub*atomic particles belong chiefly to *nuclear science* and mainly concern physicists, while the external behavior of the atom as whole is more typically the concern of chemists. (*See* CHEMICAL ——PROPERTY, CHANGE, ETC.)

NUCLEAR REACTOR. An atomic "furnace" in which atoms are fissioned in a controlled chain reaction of neutrons. It was originally called an "atomic pile" because the blocks of graphite used as a moderator were arranged like a pile of bricks. Two principal uses of reactors are to bombard particles for producing radioisotopes and for producing usable energy. This energy in the form of heat is used for making steam power, which moves the turbine of an electric generator. *See* COOLANT, CONTROL RODS, FUEL, MODERATOR, SHIELDING, which are five essentials for operating reactors. In the type known as the SWIMMING POOL REACTOR, water has three uses: as moderator, coolant, and shielding. The BREEDER reactor makes more fissionable material than it consumes in the form of fuel; that is, while using fuel it "breeds" some more.

NUCLEON. A term used when referring to a nuclear particle without specifying it. To speak of "the nucleons of a uranium atom," for example, would be to mean all the particles that such a nucleus contains (protons, neutrons, and others) without naming them over.

NUCLEONICS. The practical application of nuclear science and its techniques to other sciences and to such uses as medical, agricultural, industrial, etc.

NUCLEUS. A minute speck of matter in the center of the otherwise empty atom. The nucleus is made up of protons, neutrons, and other nucleons.

NUCLIDE. A species of atom described by the number of protons and neutrons in its nucleus. Thus the isotopes of an element can be called groups of nuclides, all having the same number of protons and hence the same atomic number.

PARTICLE ACCELERATORS. Devices to "speed up" subatomic particles, such as electrons, protons, or deuterons, thus increasing their energies. They are mainly used to study other subatomic particles. Before nuclear reactors, they were the only way to make radioisotopes in quantity. Only a few radioisotopes are now produced in this way.

PERIODIC TABLE. A chart of the elements presented in the order of their atomic numbers, showing that those elements with similar chemical and physical properties come at certain intervals.

PHOTOSYNTHESIS. The process by which plants take carbon dioxide and water from the air in the presence of sunlight to produce starches, returning oxygen to the air. All animal and human life depends on this process.

PIG. Atomic slang for heavy containers in which isotopes are shipped or stored.

POSITRON. Identical to an electron, except that it has a positive electric charge and lasts but a billionth of a second. Rare in nature, it can be produced by cosmic rays, artificial bombardment, or radioactive decay.

PROTON. A positively charged subatomic particle, found with the neutron in the atomic nucleus.

RADIOACTIVE FALLOUT. Radioactive materials carried into the air by a nuclear explosion. They are made up of fragments, or radioactive isotopes of other elements activated by the radiation from the explosion, and of the radioactive descendants of these fragments and isotopes.

RADIOACTIVE WASTE. Substances consisting mostly of the fission products from nuclear reactors, but including any waste products which are radioactive. Safe disposal of radioactive waste is a major problem in the development of atomic energy for peaceful purposes. Some of the fission products are processed to isolate useful radioisotopes.

RADIOACTIVITY. The explosion, disintegration or decay of atoms, causing the release of alpha, beta, or gamma rays. Each radioisotope disintegrates at its own rate of speed or half-life. Natural radioactivity is limited with a few exceptions to the heavier elements. Artificial radioactivity of nearly all the elements can be produced by neutron bombardment.

RADIOAUTOGRAPHY. *See* AUTORADIOGRAPHY.

RADIOCARBON DATING. The dating of substances of an organic origin, such as wood, by measuring the amount of natural radioactive Carbon-14 which they contain.

RADIOGENIC. Isotopes which are formed by the disintegration of a radioactive parent. Example: Lead-206 increases as Uranium-238 decays.

RADIOGRAPHY. Photography produced by placing an isotope source on one side of an object and a photographic film on the other side. Radiography will reveal defects in welds and castings. X-rays can also be used for radiography.

REACTOR. *See* NUCLEAR REACTOR.

ROENTGEN. A measure of the quantity of x-ray and gamma radiation. One roentgen is the amount of x-ray or gamma radiation which will produce two billion ion pairs in one cubic centimeter of dry air. The radiation from one curie (which is about one gram) of radium at one meter is 0.88 roentgen per hour, or from one curie of Cobalt-60 is 1.33 roentgen per hour per meter. The roentgen is actually a measure of energy; so each radioisotope has a different amount of radiation per curie, since the radiation from each one is different in energy. The term was selected in honor of Wilhelm Konrad Roentgen, the German physicist who discovered x-rays.

SCINTILLATION COUNTER. Like the Geiger counter, a device to detect radioactivity. It records radiation as tiny flashes of light.

SHIELD. The thick wall surrounding nuclear reactors or highly radioactive material, to protect the operators. Usually of lead or concrete.

SOURCE. A specified amount of any radioactive substance, the rays of which are being used to bombard another substance. Cobalt-60 is a gamma ray source. Krypton-85 is a beta-emitting source. *See also* NEUTRON SOURCE.

STABLE. Not radioactive.

STRINGER. A graphite block with openings to hold aluminum capsules. The capsules contain material to be made radioactive when the stringer is inserted in the nuclear reactor through an irradiation hole.

SUBATOMIC PARTICLES. Particles found in the atom, such as electrons, neutrons, and protons.

TRACER. A small amount of a radioisotope mixed with stable atoms of the same element. By a Geiger counter or other detection method, it is possible to follow the tracer and thus the behavior of the stable atoms. A few stable atoms also serve as tracers, but chemical analysis is needed to detect their presence.

TRANSMUTATION. The changing of one element to another.

TRANSURANIUM or TRANSURANIC. Terms used for the artificial elements with atomic numbers above that of uranium, which is 92. *See* list of these elements, on page 174.

## SUPPLIERS OF STABLE ISOTOPES

You may buy stable isotopes without first getting the approval of the U. S. Atomic Energy Commission. Upon request, these suppliers will send to you their price lists and explanatory circulars.

Abbott Laboratories
Oak Ridge Division
Oak Ridge, Tennessee

Atomic Research Laboratory
10717 Venice Boulevard
Los Angeles 34, California

Isomet Corporation
433 Commercial Avenue
Palisades Park, New Jersey

Isotopes Specialties Company, Inc.
170 West Providencia Street
Burbank, California

The Liquid Carbonic Division
General Dynamics Corporation
767 Industrial Road
San Carlos, California

Nuclear-Chicago Corporation
223 West Erie Street
Chicago 10, Illinois

Nuclear Consultants, Inc.
33-61 Crescent Street
Long Island City 6, New York

Oak Ridge National Laboratory
Union Carbide Nuclear Company
Isotopes Division
P. O. Box X
Oak Ridge, Tennessee

IN ENGLAND

Atomic Energy Research Establishment
Electromagnetic Separation Group
Chemistry Divid. Division, Bldg. 7
Harwell, Didcot, Berks
England

The Radiochemical Centre
White Lion Road
Amersham, Buckinghamshire
England

# INDEX